Wintering of the

Migrant Bald Eagle

in the Lower 48 States

by

Donald Spencer

Available from:

National Agricultural Chemicals Association
1155 15th Street, N.W.
Washington, D.C. 20005

Library of Congress Catalog Card Number 76-43385

Cover painting by Bob Hines

Eagle Photographs by John E. Swedberg

Photographs pp. 9, 22 Courtesy of
U.S. Fish & Wildlife Service

Copyrighted 1976

Foreword

This publication is a credit to the effort and interest of its compiler, but is most notable as a reflection of the kinds of interests and concerns a wide variety of people have about the well-being of the Bald Eagle. This noble bird, selected long ago to be symbolic of the United States, has suffered greatly as a result of man's thoughtless acts, through the effects of pollution created as man has advanced himself technologically, and because of loss of habitat.

Even so, it survives, although marginally in some parts of its range. Assurance of its survival will depend upon man, who must be willing to work — and sacrifice — in behalf of the Bald Eagle. It is evident that there are people willing to make the great effort necessary to assure the future of this majestic bird, and this publication gives insight into a small part of that willingness. Moreover, it gives indications that the Bald Eagle, like the nation it symbolizes, is adaptable, imaginative, innovative and courageous, and worthy of our best effort to save it.

Lynn A. Greenwalt
Director, U.S. Fish and Wildlife Service
Department of the Interior

Introduction

The following information on the winter-migrant bald eagle in the 48 contiguous states is by courtesy of hundreds of competent observers. Although a usable sample of the available information, there is far more to be learned than this inventory has achieved. It is the purpose of this compilation, that you, the reader, will be stimulated to prepare a more in-depth account of the winter-migrant bald eagles in your region. Be your own author, using supportive data from this compilation, acknowledging only the original contributor—not this publication.

You will find the story of the winter-migrant bald eagle very encouraging after a decade of concern about its survival. The "red carpet treatment" is really paying off.

More than that, you should be impressed with the number of organizations, and the differing management practices, that have contributed —often without design—to the welfare of this winter visitor.

Be prepared for almost unbelievable adaptations in habitat, foods, and behavior exhibited by the winter-migrant bald eagles. From a bird that obviously enjoys a daily bath and a menu of fish to a denizen of sagebrush and arid lands that provide neither water nor fish. From an indisputable scavenger, searching for "accidents to happen", to a group-hunter of agile living prey. From a bird often choosing the solitude of wilderness areas, to one tolerant (albeit wary) of automobiles, harbor traffic, and man's installations in general. Only locally does the bald eagle fit a particular mold.

Looking for bald eagles? Go west!

Donald A. Spencer

INFORMATION INPUT INTO THIS 1976 WINTERING BALD EAGLE INVENTORY

DIRECT COMMUNICATION WITH SEASON-LONG OBSERVERS:
National Wildlife Refuges: U.S. Department of the Interior
State Waterfowl Management Areas
National Forests: Regions 6 and 9
National Recreational Areas (National Parks)
Local Audubon Clubs

RESERVOIR SYSTEMS:
Bureau of Reclamation
Corps of Engineers
Tennessee Valley Authority
U.S. Department of Agriculture Soil Conservation Service

ANNUAL ONE-DAY INVENTORIES:
Mid-winter Waterfowl/eagle Inventory (State and Federal)
Audubon Christmas Bird Counts
Elton Fawk's Upper Mississippi Basin February Count

MIGRATION RECORDS:
Fixed-point Raptor Migration Station Records
Bird Banding Returns

LOCAL-INTENSIVE RESEARCH STUDIES OF WINTERING POPULATIONS:
Largely two-year studies located in Washington, Idaho, Utah, Montana, Wyoming, South Dakota, Missouri, Illinois, and Oklahoma

Three Canadian Provinces: British Columbia, Nova Scotia, and New Brunswick

RED CARPET MEASURES FOR THE BALD EAGLE

1) All programs that keep our streams, lakes, and reservoirs stocked with fish, and that restore and perpetuate runs of anadromous fish. (Even some of our fishery errors, like the introduction of carp.)

2) All programs maintaining waterfowl at the highest practical level. (Even the unintentional ineptness of some hunters.)

3) Expansion of Aquatic Habitats:
   a) Improved distribution of permanent water through reservoir and impoundment.
   b) Growth of federal and state wildlife refuge systems.
   c) A good beginning in raptor sanctuaries.

4) Public Support of Non-game Species Programs:
   a) National and state inventories of raptor populations.
   b) Intensive studies on wintering needs—University.
   c) Endangered species status for localized segments.

5) Stepped-up protection against harassment and killing.

6) Nesting sites mapped and provided with zone protection.

7) Progressive correction of chemical residue problem in foods eaten by bald eagles.

8) Changing patterns in predator control, and the taking of fur animals, to reduce hazard to raptors.

9) A solution for powerline electrocution problem.

10) Some 200 million acres in the 50 states set aside from commercial development.

11) Breakthrough in raptor reproduction-support techniques.

12) All efforts to prevent or contain wildlife diseases having possible transmission to bald eagles feeding on sick prey, such as fowl colera.

Contents

PART I:

The Central and Western States

In the northern prairie provinces of Canada, in an area strewn with timber-fringed lakes that have experienced few of the manipulated changes of civilization, is an almost ideal nesting ground for the bald eagle—except for the ice-locked winter months. But before the food supply sags to nonsustaining levels each fall, along comes a "traveling larder" also headed for more open water situations—hordes of geese and ducks. So the transition into the Mississippi valley and western states is a fairly comfortable operation—even for the young of the year who have not yet acquired any significant degree of hunting skills.

That this movement is south and southwest with only a token spread east of Lake Michigan, the Illinois River, and the lower Mississippi valley, is a choice not readily explained. But the fact remains that from the Mississippi valley westward, there is a wealth of opportunities to view exciting aggregations of winter migrant bald eagles—not found in eastern states.

In the following pages the factors that permit this wintering ground to host increasing numbers of eagles, are discussed.

1

Wintering Locations and Numbers

Each fall bald eagles from nesting areas in the interior of Canada and the northern tier of States wing south, hugging the Mississippi River to the east but fanning out broadly over the western plains that are now dotted with man-made reservoirs. The forefront of this wintering movement narrows to a wedge as it approaches the Gulf of Mexico, with the apex on the Louisiana/Texas border. Arkansas, Louisiana, and east Texas have a wealth of aquatic habitats that appear to be under-utilized by bald eagles at this time. West of this penetrating wedge most of west Texas and the southern half of New Mexico host few if any wintering bald eagles. The large impoundments on the lower Rio Grande River and the Big Bend National Park report no bald eagle sightings in the winter months.

The states of Oklahoma and Kansas have developed their water resources in the period since the "dust bowl" days of the early 1930's, greatly enhancing that area for fishing, waterfowl, and bald eagles. Practically every reservoir in the two-state area now hosts bald eagles.

The migratory front dips down the High Plains east of the Rocky Mountains into the panhandle of Texas and northern New Mexico. Here reservoirs are not so numerous and the playa (shallow) lakes tend to dry up completely about every 4 to 5 years, a less dependable wintering ground. But fluctuating water levels periodically expose the often abundant carp. Then out of nowhere come eagles that cannot be accounted for at monitored aquatic sites. As Karen Steenhof has commented in her intensive study of bald eagles in South Dakota, the carrying capacity of rangeland areas for bald eagles is underestimated. Our difficulty is in inventorying this dispersed population.

The fact that mountain areas in Colorado and northern New Mexico host wintering bald eagles at altitudes where temperatures and snow cover are anything but mild will come as a surprise. An aerial survey this past winter of the 7,000 feet high San Luis Valley in Colorado tallied some 250 bald eagles. On the other side of the Continental Divide in Colorado, along the Gunnison River, on many of the large reservoirs like the Navajo and the Vallecito—wherever there is a pocket of open water and big game carrion as a food source cushion—there will be the eagles.

Further west in Utah the leading edge of the wintering migration reaches at least as far south as the middle of the state. However, the down-sweeping arc of the Green and Colorado Rivers converging on the 180 mile long Lake Powell, followed further down the Grand Canyon by Lake Mead, is largely a non-monitored habitat. Personnel of the National Park Service report scattered sightings of bald eagles during the winter months along the canyon-wrapped waters of both lakes, but only of individuals, not groups of eagles. A few eagles may even follow the Colorado River canyon as far south as Yuma, Arizona.

Southwestern Utah and much of Nevada have little to attract bald eagles. The impoundments in westcentral Nevada—the Lahontan Valley—host between 20 to 30 bald eagles.

California has a resident nesting population of some 20 to 30 pairs of bald eagles in Plumas, Lassen, Shasta, and Trinity Counties—in the northernmost part of the state. From there north to the Canadian boundary there are scattered resident eagles. A 1975 aerial survey by Teryl G. Grubb (et al) located 100 active nests along Washington State's marine coastline. Thus western Washington, Oregon, and northern California have resident and migrant birds sharing the same wintering grounds. Much of this coastal area does not experience a great influx of migrant eagles in the fall despite the fact that the coasts of British Columbia and Alaska harbor the greatest concentration of bald eagles in North America, 30,000 to 50,000 birds. These northern coastal bald eagles redistribute regionally each winter, but there is no appreciable migration into the lower 48 states.

Migrants, possibly from some interior source do reach northern California. The wintering eagles dining at Klamath and Tule Lake National Wildlife Refuges roost communally about 10 miles south in Siskiyou County, California, forming one of the largest such roosts yet located in the West (approximately 100 birds). Other smaller groups are based at a number of northern California impoundments, with one lone outpost far to the south at Big Bear Lake near Los Angeles (nine birds in 1975-76).

MINNESOTA:

The eagle population does begin to build up during September and depending upon weather factors generally peaks in the middle of October to the first of November. Our information is somewhat sketchy, but this is a "stop over" situation and it has been assumed that crippled waterfowl from adjacent Rice Lake furnishes them food. As a rule all birds are gone by the middle of December. Occasionally one or two will hang around some open springs into January. In 1965 the peak population occurred October 3 and consisted of 13 birds—one adult and 12 immatures; 1968 the peak occurred October 29 consisting of 15 birds— 4 adults and 11 immatures; 1969 the peak occurred October 30 and consisted of 16 birds, all immatures; 1970 the peak occurred in the latter part of October consisting of 22 birds, 5 adults and 17 immatures; 1971 the peak occurred November 1 and consisted of 18 birds, 4 adults and 14 immatures. We have no figures for 1972, 1973, 1974, and 1975 but populations have been about average with departure dates toward the end of October.

Don E. Adams, Manager, Rice Lake NWR

Although few in number the total number of sightings of bald eagles during the period October through April has steadily inched upward: 1972 (18), 1973 (19), 1974 (20), and 1975 (21).

John E. Wilbrecht, Manager, Sherburne NWR

During the past ten years, bald eagles have been observed in Delta County and/or eastern half of the Upper Peninsula of Michigan during each month of the year. Winter sightings range from none to one or two per month. January is the month fewest have been observed.

William E. Taylor, Wildlife Biologist, Hiawatha National Forest

Agassiz National Wildlife Refuge does host a small number of bald eagles during the migrational seasons. Rarely, one or two will be found in the November through March freeze-up period. The migrational aggregations usually total less than ten birds, with a slight preponderance of immatures.

Joseph Kotok, Manager, Agassiz NWR

NORTH DAKOTA:

There are no bald eagles that overwinter in this vicinity, the birds just pass through in spring and fall migration.

Most birds in the spring pass through during the month of April. However, at no time do we see more than a pair of birds. We know of no concentration points in the district of bald eagles. Actual sightings of bald eagles in the spring in the month of April only amount to five or seven birds.

We do see a few more birds during fall migration, but again, not in any great numbers. Total sight observations during the fall period would range between 8 and 12 sightings. The fall sightings are usually made between the middle of October and the middle of December.

Ralph F. Fries, Project Leader, Devils Lake Wetlands, U.S.D.I.

At 4:15 p.m., 5 December, while patrolling the Downstream Public Use Area, Frank Splendoria, park Manager Trainee, saw three adult and two immature bald eagles perched in a cottonwood along the river. These eagles were observed for 18 minutes until all had flown off. On 18 December, five eagles with the same age ratio as on 5 December, were seen in the same area. The next day only three eagles, of undetermined age, were seen. After 19 December 1972 until mid-April 1973, only one pair of adults was observed below the powerhouse.

Frank A. Splendoria, U.S. Army Corps of Engineers, Garrison Dam

On 4 December 1975 Forrest Lee and Dave Gilmer of our staff conducted an aerial survey for Giant Canada Geese along the Missouri River from Fort Yates north to Riverdale (Garrison Dam). Much of the river was ice covered but certain stretches were open providing suitable habitat for several thousand mallards and several flocks of Giant Canadas. Along these open stretches of river, they also counted 7 adult bald eagles plus an immature or golden eagle.

W. Reid Goforth, Director, Northern Prairie Wildlife Research Center ter, U.S. Fish & Wildlife Service

On Audubon Refuge we usually see from one to five or six bald eagles in migration in the fall and spring, but none winter on the refuge. Audubon Refuge is located 12 miles northeast of Garrison Dam.

A few do winter on the Missouri River below Garrison Dam. The number of eagles wintering there varies from two or three to 12 or 15 or more, but this would be unusual. I have never seen more than three or four. On January 15, 1976, I saw only two adult bald eagles about a mile below the dam, but in January, 1975, I believe the State Game & Fish Department reported something like 15 or 17 eagles there. That would be unusual though.

David C. McGlauchlin, Manager, Audubon NWR

Salyer Refuge is used as a "way stop" in spring and fall migrations. However, occasionally a single bald eagle will be observed throughout the winter. For example, an adult bald eagle was frequently observed during January and February 1970, and in 1971 an immature bald eagle was seen throughout the winter.

Jon M. Malcolm, Manager, J. Clark Salyer NWR

Bald eagles do not winter in this area, in fact, they are not seen every year during the migration. The most I have seen since 1971 at one time is two. They are very rarely seen in the spring, 99 percent of the sightings are in the fall.

James W. Matthews, Manager, Arrowood NWR

No bald eagles overwinter here. We may have a golden eagle show up during the winter. Bald eagles are usually here in October, November, and early December; generally only one at a time. Our first one this spring we saw on March 24th, and that same day I saw one in migration at Bismarck.

Their appearance here coincides with the waterfowl migration, but they don't seem to spend much time in our area.
Herbert G. Troester, Manager, Tewaukon NWR

MONTANA:

Medicine Lake Refuge is primarily utilized by bald eagles as a migrational way-stop during spring and fall migrations. The last sightings are usually recorded in mid-November and first spring sightings in late March.
Jay R. Bellinger, Manager, Medicine Lake NWR

The southeastern portion of Montana bald eagles are found almost anywhere but are associated with river drainages and stands of ponderosa pine and big sagebrush. They probably occur at a density of one bald eagle every 25 square miles. In this area I have frequently counted 30 to 40 bald eagles. I would estimate the eastern half of Montana to have approximately 200 to 300 wintering bald eagles.
Terrence P. McEneaney, Biologist Technician, U.S. Fish & Wildlife Service, Sheridan, Wyoming

After the bald eagles disperse from the McDonald Creek area, numbers are seen in Bad Rock Canyon near here and about 15 miles downstream. They are here for about ten days.

There are bald eagles year-round on Flathead Lake, but not in large numbers.
Mel Ruder, Editor, Hungry Horse News, Columbia Falls

During the winters of 1974-75 and 1975-76, we did not observe bald eagle use of the refuge. In recent years bald eagle observations have been rare.

The Missouri River between Great Falls and Holter Reservoir is a wintering area for both the bald and golden eagle. Because of the relatively steep gradient and volume of flows, large sections of the river remain open even during the severest of cold spells. The waterfowl population, and of course, fish life within the river provide a food supply adequate to support a few eagles.
Lyle A. Stemmerman, Manager, Benton Lake NWR

When you see the report of our Christmas Bird Count for 1975, I believe you will find that we counted even more bald eagles on that day than we have in other years. There is no question about the increase in the population because we see immatures as well as adults.
Miss Urana Clarke, Livingston, Montana Audubon Society

Most of the wintering birds occur at Ennis Lake but can be found along most of the major streams throughout the winter (Gallatin, Madison, Jefferson, Missouri). My highest count at Ennis was 45 on April 3, 1966. At Ennis they tend to occur in winter near the inlet to the lake where there is open winter throughout most winters and cottonwoods for roosting. The area below the dam (which is down the canyon 2 miles) is open but does not seem to be a major feeding area for the eagles.

The canyon is narrow and inhabited which may inhibit the birds.

P. D. Skaar, Montana State University, Bozeman

We do not normally host any bald eagles during the winter months. We do occasionally see a few about the time our lakes freeze up and remaining waterfowl concentrate in one or two open areas. This usually occurs in early November. One or two bald eagles along with ten or more golden eagles will normally be around during this time. They harass the waterfowl a great deal; and it is presumed they pick up a few, especially weak or crippled ducks and geese. Once the freeze-up is complete, the bald eagles usually depart.

John R. Foster, Manager, Ul Bend-Bowdoin NWR

There are also from 10 to 15 bald eagles that winter each year between Livingston and Gardiner, Montana, along the Yellowstone River. This portion of the river stays open due to the warmer water from Yellowstone Park. Again we have an abundance of waterfowl on the river along with a good supply of trout and whitefish. They appear on the scene about the same time as the Billings group and departure is about the same time.

Don MacDonald, Billings, Montana, Audubon Society

NATIONAL WILDLIFE REFUGES
FLATHEAD LAKE AREA, MONTANA
1975-76

Refuge Unit	Use-Days Oct.-Dec.	Peak Numbers	Use-Days Jan.-Mar.	Peak Numbers
National Bison Range	0	—	150	3
Ninepipe NWR.	380	9	200	3
Pablo NWR.	120	3	90	2
Flathead WPA	—	4	—	3
Swan River NWR.	—	2	—	1
Smith Lake WPA	—	1	—	—
Flathead River (Columbia Falls)	—	—	(Jan. 9, '76)	21

Marvin R. Kaschke, Refuge Manager

Montana, west of the Continental Divide, is influenced in winter by air masses primarily from the Pacific Coast. These air masses bring us rather mild weather for most of the winter. The reports you may hear of wild winters in Montana come from east of the mountains. There they get very cold Canadian Polar air.

As a result of this weather pattern, we have many winters in the Missoula area when there is much open water on the Blackfoot, Bitterroot, and Clark Fork Rivers. I believe that this is the attraction for wintering eagles. We also have fairly good winter populations of waterfowl taking advantage of the same open water.

Bald eagles begin showing up here roughly in December. We think that when the big feeding concentration in Glacier Park (November, 300± birds feeding on spawning kokanees) breaks up, many of these birds drift southward to Flathead Lake and then further to the Clark Fork River drainage. They usually have departed by March or April.

There does not seem to be any "core area" or concentration. Rather, they are scattered along the river bottoms as individuals.

> *Dr. Sidney S. Frissell, Associate Professor, University of Montana: Missoula*

Most of our observations of the eagles have been immediately below Tiber Reservoir and the Marias River. We have observed several eagles each winter for the past four or five years, but other people have informed me they have seen them for eight or more years. Best estimates are based on observations, which usually are two to four each winter.

> *Marvin E. Krook, Chester, Montana*

Bald eagles are found all around Flathead Lake during the winter. Flathead Lake is 28 miles long and 7 miles wide, seldom freezing over in the winter. Last winter our club members reported seeing eagles at Yellow Bay, Woods Bay, and Polson.

Spring departures for the eagle was June 7, 1975. The first fall arrival reported was October 20, 1975.

Marcy Bishop reported seeing eagles feeding on American coots which had frozen into the ice at Polson last winter. I have seen bald eagles in the fall at Bigfork, where Swan River empties into Flathead Lake. There is a salmon run on Swan River as far as the dam, about 2 miles upstream.

The eagles are probably found at other locations on Flathead Lake during the winter, but these are the only ones about which our group knows.

> *Wanda Jamieson, Secretary, Lower Flathead Valley Bird Club*

One such area that I am familiar with is the Big Bend of the Kootenai just below Libby Dam. Our best count there one winter was 13 bald eagles. These birds feed primarily on trout and whitefish. I have seen a few on deer carcasses, but only when the carcasses are on or very near the river bank.

A few bald eagles winter along the Clark's Fork River in Sanders County. Seldom will one see more than two or three, however.

I have seen up to a dozen bald eagles along the Bitterroot River in Ravalli County during late February and March. I don't know if they winter there, however.

> *Dennis L. Flath, Nongame Biologist, Montana Department of Fish and Game*

The bald eagle arrives at the Ravalli Refuge approximately the last part of October, its population peaks to six to ten birds in December; and the birds usually depart in March.

> *R. C. Twist, Manager, Ravalli NWR*

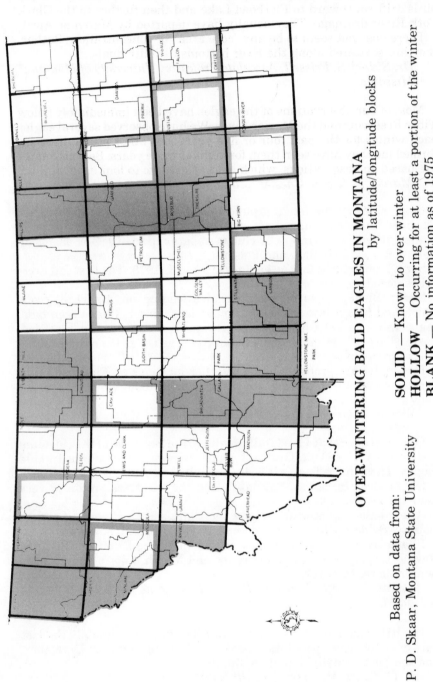

OVER-WINTERING BALD EAGLES IN MONTANA
by latitude/longitude blocks

Based on data from:
P. D. Skaar, Montana State University

SOLID — Known to over-winter
HOLLOW — Occurring for at least a portion of the winter
BLANK — No information as of 1975

During the fall the number of eagles along the 7 mile stretch of creek and river from Lake McDonald to Blankenship bridge is censused from a canoe at weekly intervals. The maximum count for each of the past eleven years is as follows:

GLACIER NATIONAL PARK

Year	Number of Birds	Peak Date
1965	189	11/19
1966	179	11/10
1967	211	11/28
1968	234	11/21
1969	373	11/20
1970	268	11/25
1971	267	11/10
1972	261	11/9
1973	357	11/21
1974	359	11/15
1975	377	11/25

Charles B. Sigler, Chief Park Ranger

WISCONSIN:

The La Crosse District of the UMR (Pools seven and eight) hosts varying numbers of bald eagles between October and March. During mid-winter, approximately January 1 through March 1, eagle numbers are generally quite low—normally one to three.

Peak numbers for the past few years have ranged from 11 to 28 in the fall and 16 to 63 (March 19, 1976) in spring. These are actual observed numbers; a few eagles probably escape observation, possibly another 10 percent would be a conservative figure for total numbers present.

Kenneth O. Butts, Manager, La Cross District, Upper Mississippi River NWR (table p17).

The bald eagle peak numbers are usually around 10-15 individuals. The eagle numbers never seemed to be very high, but it was thought there was a good turn over of birds leaving and arriving. Interestingly enough, most of the fall eagles are immature birds. Crippled waterfowl are easy targets.

Dennis W. Strom, Manager, Necedah NWR

The only period of the year that bald eagles appear on the Horicon National Wildlife Refuge is during the fall.

Peak numbers of bald eagles range from one to three.

Thomas S. Sanford, Assistant Manager, Horicon NWR

The population increased gradually until what appears to be a peak of 60 adults and three immatures on January 24, 1976. Weekly counts indicate the population fluctuates between 30 and 60 birds. These are birds actually observed. Another 10 to 20 birds could probably be added to these figures to compensate for birds not seen.

Robert E. Wilson, District Manager, Cassville District, Upper Mississippi River NWR

About 180 eagles are estimated on the district at peak periods. Actual ground observations rarely reflect the peak because of the large areas of open water available at these times, eagles are more dispersed, less readily located, and more likely to be away from observable locations than in mid-winter.

During mild portions of the winter when there is more open water, eagles may also be seen near Fountain City, Buffalo, Reick's Lake in Wisconsin, and Weaver Marsh in Minnesota.

Some observations (full district eagle counts) during the past two years are as follows:

WINONA DISTRICT, UPPER MISSISSIPPI RIVER NWR

Date	No. of Adult	No. of Immature	No. of Unknown
12/11/74	50	21	
12/18/74	55	17	
12/26/74	26	8	
01/08/75	46	9	
01/29/75	19	1	
02/06/75	18		2
02/17/75	6		
02/20/75	35		
12/03/75	24	9	2
12/10/75	50	9	
02/13/76	24	2	
03/15/76	11	2	2

Hilma L. Volk, Assistant Manager

ILLINOIS:

Crab orchard hosts a wintering concentration of eagles from October through March. Average concentration levels have increased from three eagles during the 1969-70 season to eleven during the 1974-75 season. Average levels stabilized at approximately ten birds from 1972 to the present. Peak numbers have increased similarly from six (4 immatures and 5 adults in the 1969-70 season to 23 (18 immatures and 5 adults) in the 1974-75 season. An apparent stability of peak levels at approximately 20 eagles is recognized in the use data from 1972 to the present. Peak numbers usually occur between mid-December and mid-January. Predominantly, observations have been proportionately high in immature birds.

Due to the time involved to research our records, I restricted the data to 1969 to the present. Possibly concentrations prior to 1969 may have been larger, but the trend from 1969 leads me to believe we are now hosting the larger numbers of bald eagles.

> *Wayne D. Adams, Manager, Crab Orchard NWR*

During the past ten years, the peak population observed has varied from a low of 32 birds to a high of 205 birds. Weather, census techniques, and timing of counts would probably account for most of the variability noted in peak populations. Data from the past few years indicates that peak populations on the district are stabilizing near 150 birds.

> *Thomas D. Atkins, District Manager, Upper Mississippi River NWR, Savanna District*

The best known department-managed areas where bald eagles regularly occur in numbers are: Horseshoe Lake State Park and Conservation Area in Alexander County; the Union County Conservation Area; Baldwin Lake State Park and Conservation Area; Pere Marquette State Park (Jersey County); the Sanganois Conservation Area (Cass County); Anderson Lake and Rice Lake Conservation Areas (Fulton County); and Marshall County Conservation Area. Each of these areas was covered by the 1976 Eagle Survey coordinated by Elton Fawks on February 14 and 15, of this year, as they were in past years.

The bald eagles in Illinois are generally not far from the Illinois and Mississippi rivers; and therefore, few are found at such inland locations as Lake Sangchris, Lake Shelbyville, Lake Coffeen, Lake Carlyle, and Rend Lake. In fact, I have only heard an occasional eagle being spotted at any of these inland lakes.

> *James M. Lockart, Supervisor, Division of Wildlife Resources, Illinois Department of Conservation*

The peak population was reached by 12 January (1962) approximately two weeks after maximum ice conditions and was maintained until 23 February, after which a steady decline was noticed until 1 April, when no eagles were seen. It is likely that the highest count (262) recorded on 2 February, approached the figure for the actual population of the area.

> *William E. Southern, Savannah Army Depot, Mississippi River*

Carlyle Lake—One bald eagle sighted in January, 1976. No other eagle sightings are reported for Carlyle. This lake has a large population of waterfowl during early winter. Portions of the lake usually freeze up in January, and most waterfowl leave. Total lake freeze-up rarely occurs. The dam is located near the town of Carlyle, and the general area may have too much activity for eagles to feed on fish below the dam.

Rend Lake—One bald eagle was sighted in September 1974, and one bald eagle was sighted in the winter of 1975-76. No other eagle sightings have been reported for Rend Lake. Large concentrations of ducks and geese winter at Rend. The water outlet structure is located near a large tract of bottomland timber, and human activity nearby is light in winter. However, no eagles have been seen in this vicinity. The lake rarely completely freezes over.

Lake Shelbyville—No sightings of eagles using this lake have been reported.

James Gore, Wildlife Biologist, U.S. Corps of Engineers, St. Louis

The peak population on the Louisa Division of the Mark Twain NWR of 21 bald eagles was recorded December 18th. The peak population of 11 bald eagles was recorded on December 16th on the Keithsburg Division.

Tom J. Early, District Manager, Mark Twain NWR

Populations in the area generally occur in January when between 100-150 birds are present.

Hugh H. Null, District Manager, Mark Twain NWR, Swan & Gilbert Lakes District

This past year we peaked at 35 bald eagles on January 3, 1976, 18 adults and 17 immatures.

Chautauqua use has been increasing in recent years, and in fiscal year 1975 was the second highest use area of the twelve divisions (refuge) of the Mark Twain. Peaks and total use for the past four years are as follows:

CHAUTAUQUA DIVISION, MARK TWAIN NWR

Fiscal Year	Peak	Month	Use-Days
1973	10	01	708
1974	15	02	1,155
1975	34	01	1,655
1976	35	01/3	(not complete)

Howard A. Lipke, Manager

The biggest wintering concentration of eagles I know of is on the Savanna Ordnance Depot at Savannah, Illinois, and at the lock and dam at adjoining Bellevue, Iowa. This is on the Upper Mississippi Refuge, of course. During an aerial census on February 19, 1961, I counted 208 eagles on Pools 12 and 13, most of which were on the Depot. I believe I counted about 250 in January or February of 1962 in the same area.

Herbert G. Troester, Refuge Division, U.S. Fish & Wildlife Service

MISSOURI

Peak populations generally run from 17-25 bald eagles.
Robert Dobbins, Manager, Fountain Grove WMA, Missouri

Swan Lake National Wildlife Refuge hosts bald eagles throughout the October/March period. Usually a peak of 75 to 90 eagles is reached in December.

Usually we have a preponderance of immatures; about three to four immatures for each adult. This has been noted at other refuges where there is a high concentration of eagles.
Alfred O. Manke, Manager, Swan Lake NWR

Cannon Dam and Reservoir—Winter of 1974-75, four eagle sightings. Winter of 1975-76, two eagle sightings. Project personnel could not obtain data before 1974. This area is on the Salt River in northeast Missouri. The area has large remote sections of Oak-Hickory forest with many steep, rocky bluff areas adjoining the river. No concentration of waterfowl occurs in this area.

Meramec Park Lake —No recent eagle sightings have been made in this area. Peak population of wintering eagles occurs in January in Missouri.
James F. Gore, Wildlife Biologist, U.S. Corps of Engineers, St. Louis District

LA CROSSE DISTRICT, UPPER MISSISSIPPI RIVER NWR

Month	1974 Average Peak	1975 Average Peak	1976 Average Peak
10/01-10/15	0/0	0/0	
10/16-10/31	1/1	1/1	
11/01-11/15	1/2	0/0	
11/16-11/31	3/4	0/0	
12/01-12/15	2/2	1/1	
12/16-12/31	2/4	4/4	
01/01-01/15	2/2	17/26	6/9
01/16-01/31	2/2	14/19	14/10
02/01-02/14	2/2	19/19	16/24
02/15-02/28	5/7	28/30	4/4
03/01-03/15	2/3	22/23	4/4
03/16-03/31	1/2	2/1	2/2
04/01-04/15	0/0		

Kenneth O. Butts, Manager.

BALD EAGLES
SQUAW CREEK NATIONAL WILDLIFE REFUGE

Year	Immatures	Adults	Total	Date
1976	116	106	222	01/06/76
1975	81	116	197	12/22/75
1974	92	54	146	12/09/74
1973	87	67	154	12/23/73
1972			86	12/13/72
1971	148	88	236	01/07/71
1970	164	36	200	01/01/70
1970	174	89	263	12/17-23
1969	72	19	91	01/01-07
1969	136	63	199	12/21-31
1968		70	70	12/02-08
1968	104		104	12/09-28
1967			96	01/01/67
1967			96	02/28/67
1966	79		79	12/12-31
1966		18	18	12/31/66
1966			123	02/14/66

Gerald M. Nugert, Manager

PEAK BALD EAGLE POPULATIONS ON THE
Clarence Gannon and Delair Divisions
MARK TWAIN NWR
Ten-Year Record

Winter	Cannon Refuge		Delair Division	
	Date	Peak Number	Date	Peak Number
1965-66	02/19/66	11	02/19/66	13
1966-67	03/25/67	8	03/11/67	6
1967-68	01/13/68	4	01/13/68	3
1968-69	12/28/68	2	12/28/68	6
1969-70	03/01/70	8	02/08/70	16
1970-71	11/01/70	3	01/31/71	8
1971-72	02/20/72	16	02/13/72	41
1972-73	02/03/73	9	02/03/73	25
1973-74	02/02/74	6	12/20/73	7
1974-75	12/16/74	6	12/16/74	8
1975-76	02/20/76	14	01/15/76	11

Glen R. Miller, Manager

WEEKLY VARIATIONS IN EAGLE NUMBERS 1975-76
One-Year Record
Cannon and Delair Divisions, Mark Twain NWR

	Cannon Refuge			Delair Division	
Date	Adult	Immature	Date	Adult	Immature
11/19/75		1	12/09/75		3
11/24/75		2	01/08/76	1	2
11/26/75		3	01/15/76	6	5
11/29/75		4	01/23&24	4	3
12/01/75		1	01/26/76	3	2
12/02/75		4	02/12/76		7
12/09/75		4	03/01/76		4
12/11/75	1	4			
12/14/75	4	6			
12/16/75		8			
12/19-26	2	11			
02/12/76	1	1			
02/13/76	4	7			
02/17/76	4	2			
02/18-19	3	2			
02/20/76	6	8			
02/23/76	1	6			
02/24/76	1	11			
02/27/76	1	2			
03/01/76	2	2			
03/03/76	2	1			
03/04/76		2			
03/05/76		4			

Glen R. Miller, Manager

Peak bald eagle numbers sighted on Mingo NWR are recorded as to the following years:

Year	No. of Birds	Year	No. of Birds	Year	No. of Birds
1965	6	1969	11	1973	18
1966	21	1970	10	1974	25
1967	12	1971	21	1975	22
1968	24	1972	25	1976	28

Gerald L. Clawson, Manager

During periods of extreme cold weather and consequent freeze-ups, there definitely is a buildup of eagles around the water holes kept open by the ducks and geese. It is during these times that our peak populations occur with the most ever observed and recorded being in 1974 when a total of 53 eagles were counted on January 10th. If cold weather persists and ducks and geese move on, the eagles also leave with only a few remaining to clean up the cripples.

Noel G. Seek, Assistant Manager, Schell-Osage WMA, Missouri

IOWA:

Bald eagles are quite scarce at Union Slough. Between October and March, the only bald eagles, ranging from 1-4 birds, occur in October paralleling the migrant waterfowl concentrations. Generally during the spring waterfowl migration in April more eagles are observed than in October. Thus, a peak number of about 5 is most apt to occur in April. occur in April.

Jack C. Womble, Manager, Union Slough NWR

SOUTH DAKOTA:

A review of the records of bald eagle peak populations on Lake Andes National Wildlife Refuge since 1952 reveals sharp yearly differences from repeated lows of less than ten birds to a high of better than 60 in 1971.

Karen Steenhof, Research Biologist, Lake Andes NWR

The numbers of eagles in the peak periods were reported as follows:

Lewis and Clark Lake	30-40
Lake Francis Case	80+
Lake Sharpe	25-30
Lake Oahe	20-30
Lake Sakakawea	12-17
Fort Peck Lake	8

All of our main stem projects reported that bald eagles overwinter in their tailrace areas. These areas downstream of the dams have had overwintering populations of eagles since the projects have been in operation. Fort Peck beginning operation in 1943 and the last project completed, Lake Sharpe, beginning operation in 1964.

Russell L. Bywater, Omaha District, Corps of Engineers, U.S. Army

Only an occasional bald eagle is recorded at Pocasse NWR, and there is definitely no overwintering population. We do not have good data on the few eagles that do come through the Pocasse area as it is an unmanned station.

Twenty miles east of Pierre, South Dakota as many as 96 bald eagles have been observed late in the fall feeding on crippled geese in front of McDowell's shooting area.

At Sand Lake National Wildlife Refuge, we observe from six to twelve bald eagles during both spring and fall waterfowl migration periods.

William C. Blair, Manager, Sand Lake NWR, Columbia, South Dakota

As a rule, bald eagles do not concentrate in any large numbers on the Waubay NWR or surrounding area. We do have spring and fall migrants numbering two or three that usually arrive in March or April and pass through again during the months of October and November.

Robert R. Johnson, Manager, Waubay NWR

LaCreek National Wildlife Refuge does play host to a few migrating bald eagles during both spring and fall and sometimes plays winter host as well. A peak of seven bald eagles were observed on the refuge during January, 1976, waterfowl/eagle count. Hunting is very light here so there are few crippled waterfowl, but bald eagles do take wintering waterfowl as well as fish (mostly carp).

Harold H. Burgess, Refuge Manager, LaCreek NWR

The bald eagle population peaked last fall at 136 on December 15 on the river between Fort Randall Dam and the Nebraska border. A peak roosting population of 28 occurred on the south unit of Lake Andes in January and February.

Al Trout, Assistant Refuge Manager, Lake Andes NWR

NEBRASKA:

The average number for the last few years has been about four or five birds. However, during this last spring we had fifteen birds staying with us.

Robert J. Wicht, Manager, Lillian Annette Rowe Audubon Wildlife Sanctuary

WYOMING:

We have some overwintering birds in and adjacent to the park. They are most conspicuous in late February and March, use carrion from elk and bison as food sources on the Madison and Yellowstone Rivers, and might represent 2-3 dozen birds. Numbers appear to increase in April in some years (no doubt including our nesting population) depends upon carrion sources, and waterfowl availability.

Dough Houston, Biologist, Yellowstone National Park

There are many areas around the state which winter sizable concentrations of bald eagles. However, these areas might encompass several hundred square miles. Also, in a few localities eight to fourteen eagles might live together for a period of several months before returning to northern nesting areas.

George F. Wrakestraw, Supervisor, Waterfowl Management, Wyoming Game & Fish Department

KENTUCKY:

Ballard Wildlife Management Area is located 35 miles west of Paducah, Kentucky, and adjacent to the Ohio River. Running 8 miles south of Dam 53, we are also 7 miles north of the confluence of the Ohio and Mississippi Rivers. The area covers 8,000 acres, and it is a major wintering habitat for geese.

I have been resident manager here since 1959. Our goose population has grown from 4,000 to 100,000 at times during the winter. As the goose flock increased, so did the bald eagles until 1966 when we had 16. Since that time our goose flock has increased, but the number of bald eagles has decreased. During this past winter (1975-76) our population was down to eight.

James O. Moynahan, Manager, Ballard WMA, Kentucky

TENNESSEE:

Prior to 1972 the wintering population of bald eagles on Reelfoot Lake, Tennessee, had peaked at about 45-48 birds for many years. Since then we have peaked at something over 100 birds each winter.

Wendell E. Crews, Manager, Reelfoot NWR

Bald eagles have wintered on Tennessee NWR since 1950. The number has fluctuated from 8-40 generally following waterfowl peaks. The eagles have attracted numerous visitors over the years. Golden eagles also winter at Tennessee NWR.

Vandiver L. Childs, Refuge Manager, Tennessee NWR

The only recorded bald eagle use of Hatchie Refuge since its activation in 1965 was during September, 1974. The adult bird was noted on several occasions during that month.

Dennis B. Jordan, Refuge Manager, Hatchie NWR

We have observed eagles on virtually all of the larger reservoirs although certain lakes support greater numbers for longer time periods than do other lakes. The following is a summary of peak wintering populations for each reservoir for the last three years:

TVA SYSTEM OF RESERVOIRS

Reservoir	Number of Bald Eagles
Cherokee	1 to 2
Douglas	1 to 2
Upper Holston Lakes	1 to 3
Norris	2 to 4
Melton Hill	3 to 5
Watts Bar	2 to 5
Chickamauga	2 to 3
Guntersville	5 to 10
Wheeler	1 to 2
Pickwick	1 to 2
Kentucky and Barkeley (Land Between The Lakes Portion)	15 to 25

Thomas H. Ripley, Director, Division of Wildlife Development, TVA

BALD EAGLES ON CROSS CREEKS NWR

1967 — 1 mature (First recorded eagle on refuge)
1968 — 2 mature
1969 — 2 mature/1 immature
1970 — 2 mature
1971 — 4 mature/3 immature
1972 — 4 mature/3 immature
1973 — 2 mature/2 immature
1974 — 3 mature/1 immature
1975 — 3 mature/1 immature

Samuel W. Barton, Manager

KANSAS:

On the Glen Elder State Game Management Area, bald eagle numbers followed the abundance of waterfowl.

Date	Mallards	Bald Eagles
11/14/75	25,000	0
11/28/75	150,000	0
12/12/75	100,000	6
12/26/75	135,000	26
01/23/76	150,000	35
02/06/76	95,000	25
02/24/76	15,000	5

Donald R. Roy and Ken Tompkins, Game Biologist, Kansas State

Peak numbers have varied markedly from year to year:

Webster Reservoir: 1963 (80), 1966 (9), 1967 (12), 1969 (12), 1970 (2), 1972 (1), 1973 (5), 1975 (3).

Cedar Bluff Reservoir: 1964 (40), 1966 (6), 1969 (3), 1971 (12), 1972 (9), 1973 (24), 1975 (5).

In the winter of 1958-1959, we had a peak at Webster Reservoir of 130 eagles. Why they were there I do not know, but we did have a crappie winter kill.

Back in 1958-1959 we did not have a shad population in the reservoir, and since then we have had some winter kills of shad and no large fluctuations of eagles. In my opinion, the fish kill did not bring the eagles in.

Earl Richardson, Area Game Manager, Cedar Bluff WMA

I believe that you will find that the peak numbers of bald eagles using Cheney WMA is more closely related to the massive cold waves which sweep across the great plains than any particular month of the season. As a rule February is our coldest month, however, bald eagles do not follow the calendar.

My records tend to bear this out. In February, 1974, there were 105 bald eagles on the area for the peak of that season. In 1975 the peak occurred on March 7 with 18 bald eagles; and for this year, 1976, the peak occurred on January 9 with 11 bald eagles.

February, 1974, was noted for a severe cold spell of long duration over much of the Midwest.

Ken Garrigues, Manager, Cheney WMA, Kansas

First I should state that eagle counts are recorded along with bi-weekly waterfowl counts at the lake. During the past two winters while the lake was dry, a few eagles (5-10), have remained in the vicinity.

Lake McKinney normally winters 80-100 thousand ducks, mostly mallards, in years with normal water levels. Even in dry years there are usually 5-10 thousand mallards wintering on local ponds and the river, within a radius of 10 miles of the lake. There is always some waterfowl hunting going on in season, and assuming a normal crippling rate, there should be ducks available to eagles every winter. When the lake is dry, waterfowl hunting is more dispersed. Possibly this accounts for the eagles being more dispersed also.

Lake McKinney has been dry six or seven times in the last 70 years, roughly every eight to eleven years. Prior to 1974, the lake was dry last in 1966. I might speculate that eagle numbers are high only in years with normal water levels, and numbers build up slowly after dry periods.

The Arkansas River is about 1.5 miles south of Lake McKinney, and this area provides an alternate roosting and feeding area.

Robert J. Price, District Game Biologist, Lake McKinney WMA, Kansas

Population varies quite a bit, but as I recall, I usually saw around 25 to 30 eagles on my count day. Half of these would have been bald's. I can remember a high count one day where I saw 40 some eagles, and over 20 were bald's.

Bruce C. Peters, District Game Protector, Lakin, Kansas

Wintering waterfowl flocks, primarily mallards, on Tuttle Creek vary with habitat conditions of the area primarily and secondarily with population trends. Wintering flocks usually peak in mid-December and vary from 2,000 or 3,000 birds to 30,000 or 40,000.

When wintering duck numbers are good, that is, 10,000 to 15,000, eagles are common. They are less common with a decrease in ducks. The topography of Tuttle Creek Reservoir is steeply sloping grass covered hills rising to 200 feet above the lake along a 20-mile length of reservoir. It seems conducive to eagles. They rest and perch in lakeside trees and in riparian timber of woody drainages in grasslands. The eagles are frequently observed on the ice near duck flocks in winter.

R. E. McWhorter, Regional Game Supervisor, Tuttle Creek WMA, Kansas

BALD EAGLE WINTERING POPULATIONS
QUIVIRA NATIONAL WILDLIFE REFUGE
Stafford, Kansas

Year	First Seen	Peak Population Immature	Adult	Total	11-12 Date
1956-57	11/21			4	12/03
1957-58	11/25			6	11/25
1958-59	12/05			22	11/25
1959-60	11/01			12	12/31
1960-61	12/02			45	12/21
1961-62	10/18	19	21	40	12/31
1962-63	10/29	13	34	47	12/31
1963-64	11/20			26	12/31
1964-65	11/17			25	12/29
1965-66	10/27			31	12/29
1966-67	11/16			9	12/22
1967-68	11/12			14	12/11
1968-69	10/08			12	11/25
1969-70	10/22	13	12	25	12/25
1970-71	10/19	24	6	30	11/29
1971-72	10/19	10	9	19	12/20
1972-73	10/12	14	9	23	12/17
1973-74	10/19	41	20	61	12/10
1974-75	10/11	19	7	26	12/17
1975-76	10/05	9	9	18	12/22

Charles R. Darling, Manager

BALD EAGLE WINTERING POPULATIONS
Quivera National Wildlife Refuge
Stafford, Kansas

Year	Last Seen	Peak Population Immature	Adult	Total	01-03 Date
1956-57	02/15			10	01/01
1957-58	01/02			8	01/02
1958-59	03/07			22	01/01
1959-60	04/08			22	01/00
1960-61	03/29	16	34	50	01/18
1961-62	04/06	19	21	40	01/01
1962-63	03/20	13	34	47	01/01
1963-64	03/18			50	01/06
1964-65	03/31			56	02/00
1965-66	03/30			31	01/13
1966-67	03/30			17	01/17
1967-68	04/12			17	02/05
1968-69	03/18			12	02/10
1969-70	03/28	13	12	25	01/01
1970-71	04/06	8	6	14	01/02
1971-72	03/21	13	9	22	01/17
1972-73	04/17	17	9	26	01/01
1973-74	04/08	39	19	58	01/27
1974-75	04/94	16	4	20	01/08
1975-76	03/03	12	6	18	01/06

Charles R. Darling, Manager

This year the maximum number sighted in one day was 27 with other day sightings of 20. I would estimate the population using John Redmond Reservoir and Flint Hills NWR near 30.

Joe L. Plumer, Biologist Technician, Flint Hills NWR

Below is the peak numbers of bald eagles for the past few years, normally we have about 25 percent more golden eagles than we do bald eagles.

Year	Winter Migration	Spring Migration
1965	3	13
1966	6	12
1967	5	11
1968	6	7
1969	1	7
1970	4	4
1971	4	7
1972	11	7
1973	21	2
1974	12	2
1975	5	10

Keith S. Hansen, Manager, Kirwin NWR

OKLAHOMA:

Mr. Frank Bunch (Goddard Youth Camp, Route 1, Sulphur, Oklahoma, 73086) says there were 7 to 14 bald eagles along the south side of Arbuckle Lake during the period October-March, 1975. Mr. Bunch also mentioned that five to ten bald eagles were at Oil Creek Lake about 10 miles southeast of Arbuckle Lake this past winter.

E. Macdougall Palmer, Interpretative Specialist, Chickasaw National Recreation Area

Bald eagles have been sighted on almost every reservoir in Oklahoma. A figure of 550 to 600 eagles is a minimum population estimate.

James W. Lish, MS Thesis (1975), Oklahoma State University

Our highest eagle count in the winter of 1974-75 was ten. Our highest count in 1975-76 was twelve. Yes, there has been a slight upward trend in eagle use. Our eagles are most noticeable during the goose hunting season when they move into our protected areas to feed on crippled geese. This year we held between 6 and 12 eagles on the refuge from early November until late February.

Jerry C. Sturdy, Assistant Manager, Tishomingo NWR

These eagles usually appear in late October with the population peak of about 35 occurring around January 10. We have weekly census records on eagles beginning in 1972.

Robert H. Stratton, Jr., Manager, Sequoyah NWR

The Washita NWR has over the past five years become one of the most important waterfowl wintering areas in the Central Flyway. In particular, Canada goose populations have increased from a winter average of 15,000 to 20,000 in late 1960's to over 35,000 average with a peak of 52,500 this past year. Many of these birds we feel are drawn from the Salt Plains Refuge where crop conditions have been poor for the past few years. As the geese have shifted from Salt Plains, I expect to see a similar shift of part of the wintering eagle population since I suspect that crippled geese from adjacent hunts constitute an important part of their diet. This shift to Washita would, of course, be an "accidental" discovery by the birds. Hunting around the Washita NWR is increasing tremendously each year. Therefore, the opportunity for eagles to catch easy prey is also increasing. However, to date we have only observed lone bald eagles sporadically.

J. Brent Giezentanner, Manager, Washita NWR

COLORADO:

There are bald eagles that winter over around Blue Mesa and Morrow Point Lakes. Cliff Coghill, Wildlife Conservation Officer with the Colorado Division of Wildlife, reports a high count during the winter of 1975-76 of four eagles at Roaring Judy, and eight eagles from Gunnison to Curecanti Creek.

James W. Packard, Superintendent, Curecanti National Recreation Area, National Park Service

Wintering bald eagle populations are now common on the Monte Vista Refuge, as well as in the entire San Luis Valley which is located in southcentral Colorado. A peak population of thirty to forty birds will be present on the refuge sometime between the middle of December and the middle of January.

You may be interested to know that Erv Boeker of the U.S. Fish & Wildlife Service in Denver; Eugene Knoder, who is with Audubon Society in Denver, and Jerry Craig, Raptor Biologist, Colorado Division of Wildlife, flew aerial transects of the valley during the week of January 30 of this year, and from this transect it was estimated that between 200 and 250 bald eagles were in the valley at that time.

Charles R. Bryant, Manager, Monte Vista NWR

The following list of sightings and dates were on Pathfinder NWR:

Number of Bald Eagles	Date
2	04/74
11	03/74
2	10/73
1	09/73
2	04/73
20	03/73
3	12/72
2	04/72
15	03/72

Pathfinder Refuge has never had a resident refuge manager. On Hutton Lake NWR there have been sightings every march of one to two bald eagles each year. Arapaho had two sightings; one in March 1974 and the other in January 1973.

V. Carrol Donner, Manager, Arapaho NWR

Specific Areas	Bald Eagles
Durango Christmas Bird Count (Section of Animas and Florida Rivers)	9
Vallecito Reservoir (October/November) peak count	25
Navajo Reservoir (Peak Count—9 Adults/6 Immatures)	15

Bald eagles can be found along most any river or body of water from October through December, then after the first of the year only along major water ways.

All these areas are far enough apart so I feel these are different populations and not the same birds moving from place to place. With an "off the top of the head" estimation, I would say there are between 25 and 35 wintering bald eagles in the southwestern counties of Colorado. These counties include Montezuma, La Plata, and Archuleta.

Richard Stransky, Durango Audubon Society

ARKANSAS:

The average wintering population on our area is about 12 eagles, usually in the ratio of about nine immatures to three adults. This winter, however, a sighting was made of sixteen eagles on January 24, which included fourteen immatures and two adults. This is the largest number of bald eagles seen on the refuge in six years.

When considering our wintering eagle population, one must also consider the Arkansas River and Lake Dardanelle from about Clarksville down river to a few miles past the refuge. We fly this area in January when funds permit and usually spot approximately 25 to 30 bald eagles. In contrast to the refuge, most birds seen on Lake Dardanelle are adults, thereby making the total area population in an approximate 50:50 ratio of immature:adult.

Populations seem to be relatively stable when compared with records going back 10-15 years.

Paul D. Daly, Manager, Holla Bend NWR

From three to five bald eagles winter on the White River Refuge from late November until mid-February each year. This number has not varied much for the past 15 years. As far as I know this is considered to be the Northern species.

Raymond R. McMasters, Manager, White River NWR

Bald eagle use of the refuge is usually confined to the periods when waterfowl concentrations are greatest (November-February). However, even then they are observed very infrequently. From July, 1971, to present, only 108 use days have been recorded for this species with three being the peak population.

John H. Doebel, Manager, Wapanocca NWR

LOUISIANA:

We have kept eagle observations of the state for a number of years; but during the winters of 1971-72, 1972-73, and 1973-74, we ran an observation survey of the entire state. This survey involved well over one hundred competent observers scattered throughout the state. The results of this study indicate a scattering of bald eagles throughout the state during the months of December, January, February, and early March. The total number of birds observed in Louisiana prior to and proceeding these months drops quickly, so we assume that the majority of eagles found in Louisiana during midwinter are migrant birds.

The total number of all eagles in Louisiana at one time is more numerous in January and February. This is when winter is usualy at its worst, so I feel it is logical to assume that our population is augmented by a considerable number of wintering birds.

During early February, 1975, 28 bald eagles were observed by two competent observers at one time below the Toledo Bend Lake spillway. I have seen 18 or more birds at one time on more than one occasion. At one time, there was a communal roost located approximately 3 miles from the dam, which was utilized by at least 25 individuals for roosting. This lake is at least 70 miles long, and we receive reports from one end of the lake to the other. I would speculate that in some years we may have as high as 40 to 50 birds wintering in this area.

The three other major concentration areas for wintering brids are along the Ouachita River in Morehouse Parish (6-7 birds); the Spring Bayou area of Madison and Tensas Parish (5-12 birds); and the Catahoula Lake area of Catahoula and LaSalle Parishes (3-7 birds). Most of the other large impoundments in Louisiana have at least one or more birds on them during the winter if only for a brief period of time. If I had to guess the number of wintering birds in Louisiana during an average year, it would be between 50 and 75 individuals, with this figure reaching 100 during some severe winters.

S. Ray Aycock, Jr., Wildlife Biologist, U.S. Fish & Wildlife Service

TEXAS:

After speaking with some ranchers and trappers in this area, we were unable to find anyone that had seen a bald eagle in this area. We do have golden eagles here, but no bald eagles have been recorded.

Harold W. Timmons, Acting Superintendent, Amistad NRA

BALD EAGLE USE DAYS ON
BUFFALO LAKE NATIONAL WILDLIFE REFUGE

Year	Days	Year	Days
1959	560	1968	125
1960	80	1969	145
1961	245	1970	20
1962	165	1971	25
1963	145	1972	355
1964	160	1973	616
1965	150	1974	63
1966	110	1975	35
1967	300		

Peak numbers range from one to six with the greatest one time peak number being sixteen on January 15, 1973.

Larry Wynn, Buffalo Lake NWR, Umbarger, Texas

Muleshoe—Two adult bald eagles were on Muleshoe from November 19, 1975 through December 3, 1975. Five adult bald eagles were on Muleshoe December 3, 1975 through January 14, 1976. Six adult bald eagles and one immature were on Muleshoe from January 14, 1976 through February 29, 1976. All seven were in the same tree.

Bert E. Blair, Manager, Muleshoe NWR

We first noted eagles at Lake O' the Pines in the early 1960's and have counted 17 different birds using the lake.

Our rangers found one nest located on the upper reaches of the lake. It is not being used at present.

The eagles are seen on all parts of the lake but seem to use the lower half of the lake to feed. We have one high point called Lock Mountain that seems to be their favorite area.

O. L. Stafford, Manager, Lake O' the Pines, U.S. Corps of Engineers

Bald eagles start arriving at lake Meredith in late October and have been observed into late March. Christmas bird counts in the two circles covering Lake Meredith reveal:

1973	6 (4 adults, 2 immatues)
1974	20 (10 adults, 10 immatures)
1975	15 (6 adults, 9 immatures)

Shortly after the first of the year, fifteen bald eagles (eight adults and seven immatures) were observed on private land upstream from Lake Meredith.

Larry K. Neilson, Acting Superintendent, Lake Meredith National Recreational Area

Warren is a 70-acre lake centered in a rice farming area just to the West of Houston, Texas. Huge wintering populations of geese and ducks use Warren Lake as a night resting area while fanning out widely during the day to feed in the rice stubble.

The 18 bald eagles seen at one time this past winter (at Warren Lake) is the greatest single sighting ever reported. We believe there are 15-20 eagles in this area every winter, with 60 to 80 percent immatures. There are no other places where eagles are seen in the Houston area.

Dan H. Hardy, Houston, Texas, (Publication: The Spoonbill)

Bald eagles have never used the refuge regularly. There are usually at least one or two observations of bald eagles on or near the refuge in winter. This year an immature was reported on the refuge in November and near the refuge this month.

Since the development of large reservoirs in east Texas, the trend seems to be fewer eagles on the upper coast.

Russel W. Clapper, Manager, Anahuac NWR

NEW MEXICO:

With regard to sighting of 57 bald eagles at Wheeler lake on February 19, 1975, I can report the following: The figure of 57 bald eagles may be an overestimate, but there were at least 35 birds present around that small lake (perhaps 10 to 15 acres). Bald eagles winter regularly in that area and down the Mora River to the Canadian River.

John Hubbard, Project Leader, Endangered Species Program, New Mexico Department of Game & Fish

Two adult bald eagles were on Grulla from October 15, 1975, through March 2, 1976.

Bert E. Blair, Jr., Manager, Grulla NWR

The Las Vegas Refuge annually hosts several wintering bald eagles. Numbers have varied over the years from three or four up to a high of ten individuals. Just where these birds come from is not certain. They could be northern birds or eagles that have nested in the higher country of New Mexico and Colorado and migrant to lower elevations. There really hasn't been a population trend either up or down over the past nine years.

Fred L. Bolwahnn, Manager, Las Vegas NWR

On February 19, 1975, two employees of the New Mexico Game & Fish Department (District Supervisor Rueben Gonzales and Endangered Species Specialist Marshall Conway) visited this park. On the road into the park (New Mexico Highway 477), they had spotted a large contingent (57) of bald eagles feeding at Wheeler Lake. While the head count varied, this large gaggle of eagles were observed by our staff members for perhaps a fifteen to twenty day period.

Apparently this shallow lake supported a good population of trash fish, and the birds made a feeding stopover on their migration. However, we have no unique habitat or food supply that causes bald eagles to maintain any kind of routine residence here.

Ross R. Hopkins, Superintendent, Fort Union National Monument

During the past five years, we have not known more than one bald eagle to use the refuge during the winter months. This year one immature eagle spent the winter, and one adult passed through (spent one day).

Larry R. Ditto, Assistant Manager, Bosque del Apache NWR

The Maxwell National Wildlife Refuge was established in 1967. The first three years only a few bald eagles were noted using the area. Since 1970 an average population of eight bald eagles have used the refuge from mid-November to mid-March. We feel that the added factor of protection has attributed to sustained use as well as the food supply.

The peak population of bald eagles, 1970-76, has varied from 8 to 16 birds. This peak occurs between February 15th and March 4th. It is felt that this late peak may indicate that the refuge is used as a staging area prior to their northward migration.

Milton B. Suthers, Assistant Manager, Maxwell NWR

IDAHO:

Approximately twenty bald eagles winter on or near Camas National Wildlife Refuge. About 30 to 40 eagles were on the Henry's Fork and South Fork Snake River this year.

Jack L. Richardson, Manager, Camas NWR

I supplied the original figure of 15 wintering birds and believe it to be reliable. As far as we know, there are no summering birds in this area. I don't believe any nesting occurs in the upper Salmon drainage. The birds use the river from Challis to the mouth of the Middle Fork, a distance of approximately 100 miles and an additional 90 miles of the Middle Fork of the Salmon River.

Walter L. Brodie, Regional Game Biologist, Idaho Department of Fish & Game

This is just a way stop for the bald eagles. They do not spend the winter here as do the golden eagles. This migration does not involve a large number of birds, but it is very regular. The numbers of eagles peak usually in April, and twenty would be the highest of peaks. Generally one or two pair will appear at the end of March with the first migrating ducks. As the migrant waterfowl numbers increase, the numbers of eagles also increase.

Russel Hoffman, Manager, Grays Lake & Bear Lake NWR

At these times we have one to four bald eagles present at various times, and I believe much of this use is by wanderers from the concentrations around Pend Oreille and Coeur d'Alene Lakes to the south where Idaho Fish & Game see 50 to 100 on census flights for waterfowl. Everything is pretty well frozen over during the December to February period, and only an occasional eagle is observed here.

Refuge records from past years (1965) indicate the same general pattern of sightings of less than four bald eagles at any time, usually during the fall and spring months. No specific "peaks" during these times.

The upper Kootenai River, 20 to 30 miles to the east, receives use by six to ten eagles during the late fall and early spring.

Delano A. Pierce, Manager, Kootenai NWR

We do not host many, but some do spend the winter around the reservoir. As the refuge is frozen by mid-December each year, I feel the bald eagles are mostly following the migrating waterfowl as a few can always be seen sitting on the periphery of large duck concentrations in open areas of the reservoir. Prior to freeze-up, the bald eagles can be observed sitting in Cottonwoods around the reservoir looking for fish.

I know of no bald eagles wintering on Magic or Mormon Reservoirs. The reservoirs usually freeze between mid-November and mid-December and do not normally open up until about the latter part of April.

Robert J. Bell, Regional Fisheries Manager, Idaho Department of Fish and Game

Concentrations of bald eagles in the Rupert and Burley areas are a result of Snake River and Snake River impoundments; notably Lake Walcott and Milner during the period of November through march.

I have counted as high as eleven bald eagles on Lake Walcott around open water and as high as nine on the Snake River and Milner impoundment. The birds can be observed perched in cottonwood trees along the shoreline and on feeding flights. Bald eagles have also been observed at the mouth of North Heglar canyon in Cassia County and in the Malta area around Blackpine Mountain.

Dan Poppleton, Conservation Officer, Idaho Fish & Game Department

I have seen no evidence indicating that wintering bald eagles in our region are here because of a highly available fishery situation. Following is a list of bald eagle wintering areas, estimates of numbers, approximate time of year, and some speculation as to why the birds favor these areas.

South Fork of the Boise River from Rocky Bar downstream to and including Anderson Ranch Reservoir, Camas, and Elmore counties:

> Estimated number of bald eagles—15 to 20
> Time period— November through March
> Food source—Some fish but primarily carrion (deer and elk winter loss) and predator loss.

Snake River from Twin Falls to Bliss Dam:

> Esitmated number of bald eagles—15
> Time period—November through March
> Food source—Some fish but primarily waterfowl and crippling loss from hunting.

Big Wood River from Bellevue downstream to and including Magic Reservoir and Silver Creek, Blaine County:

Estimated number of wintering bald eagles—10
Time period—Mid-October through mid-April
Food source—Fish and waterfowl, primarily crippling loss due
to hunting.

Foothill areas of Blaine, Gooding, Lincoln, and Elmore counties and
east-west area comprising townships 2, 3, and 4 South.

Estimated number of bald eagles—30+
Time period—Mid-October through December
Food source—Mammal prey species and carrion, primarily big
game. I have seen them feeding on deer gut piles several times.
Ted Chu, Conservation Officer, Idaho Fish & Game Department

BALD EAGLES
MINIDOKA NWR

Year	First Arrival	Peak No.	Month	Last Seen
1975	Late November	7	December	Early April
1974	Early December	7	December	Early March
1973	Early November	7	December	Late March
1972	Mid-November	12	December	Mid-February
1971	Mid-November	11	November	Late March
1970	Late October	6	November	Mid-February
1969	Mid-October	10	December	Early February
1968	Late September	9	December	Early April
1967	Early September	7	December	Early April
1966	Mid-November	6	December	Late March

John D. Hill, Manager

UTAH:

At present, I'm more familiar with the bald eagles in northeastern
Utah. In this part of the state, as many as 24 bald eagles, both mature
and immature birds, have been counted on a small lake containing a
large population of waterfowl; after the lake freezes the eagles leave.
This past year I ran a bald eagle count from Flaming Gorge to Browns
Park. During December and January approximately 20 bald eagles
were wintering in the area. In March there were approximately 35
bald eagles, and in April most had left with only a few immatures seen.

Along the Wasatch Front, I observed a kettle of 50 plus bald eagles
moving approximately 1,000 to 1,500 feet above the Wasatch escarp-
ment. This was in March. Over 120 bald eagles were counted perched
in trees at one of our waterfowl marshes the previous week.
*Phillip W. Wagner, Raptor Biologist, Utah Division of Wildlife Re-
sources*

In 1974 there were but two adult bald eagles at the Desert Lake Wildlife Management Area. This increased to seven (two adults and five immatures) in 1975.

In 1975 nine bald eagles were recorded at Gordon Creek Wildlife Management Area. This was a different group than at Desert Lake WMA as both groups were observed on the same day.

Larry B. Dalton, Wildlife Biologist, Utah Division of Wildlife Resources

The average peak number of 10 to 20 counted in past years was exceeded on December 2, 1975, when 47 bald eagles were found. Many of the eagles use the refuge a very short time, so it is possible that a greater number of eagles have migrated through in other years but were not counted at their peak. Less than ten bald eagles stay all winter.

The peak numbers recorded during migratory periods in the spring are as follows:

> March 18, 1966: 69 bald eagles
> March 15, 1967: 69 bald eagles
> March 26, 1969: 72 bald eagles
> March 20, 1971:   4 bald eagles   From : annual refuge
> March 12, 1972: 11 bald eagles   narrative reports.
> March 25, 1973: 30 bald eagles   1954-65 also
> March 15, 1974: 102 bald eagles   available.
> March 1, 1975: 92 bald eagles
> March 18, 1976: 78 bald eagles

Ned I. Peabody, Mgr., Bear River Migratory Bird Refuge

As many as 49 eagles have been counted on any one day with 25 to 30 not uncommon.

Noland F. Nelson, Superintendent, Ogden Bay WMA, Utah

We usually winter approximately five to fifteen birds.

Timothy H. Provan, Superintendent, Farmington Bay WMA, Utah

Bald eagles, approximately five to ten birds winter here in Brown's Park, Utah portion. Dates normally fall from around October 20 to mid-March, peak population around mid-January. The Green River is their main attraction here more so than the refuge.

F. Neil Folks, Superintendent, Brown's park WMA, Utah

Clear Lake Waterfowl Management Area does host bald eagles during the period from mid-October through mid-March each winter, but only few in numbers. It is very unusual to sight more than two or three eagles at a time on the area. The sightings are erratic indicating that they may be wintering in this area, but only visit occasionally while foraging.

Don E. Neilson, Superintendent, Clear Lake WMA, Utah

I cannot provide you with much information about bald eagles on Public Shooting Grounds or Salt Creek. I have observed them on the areas but not with regularity. The few which I have observed have been on Public Shooting Grounds during the months of February and March when the spring migration is in full swing.

Dallas Taylor, Superintendent, Public Shooting Grounds WMA

Bald eagles have been present in the following numbers at Fish Springs National Wildlife Refuge.

Winter 1971-72: 1-3 bald eagles
Winter 1972-73: 2-4 bald eagles   Condensed from
Winter 1973-74: 2-3 bald eagles   monthly count
Winter 1974-75: 4-6 bald eagles   records.
Winter 1975-76: 4-5 bald eagles

Michael W. Perkins, Asst. Mgr. Fish Springs NWR, Gandy, Utah

We usually have two or more (never more than five) bald eagles present on an on-and-off basis every winter at Ouray National Wildlife Refuge.

Three bald eagles were present daily on or around the refuge during the period October, 1975, through February, 1976. However, they had been present prior to October, so couldn't be considered as fall migrants.

The most intersting bald eagle feature of this area is the congregation of 18 to 28 birds on Pelican Lake in late February through mid-March. They are attracted during the period of time when the ice is breaking up on the lake and winter-killed bass and bluegill are available as a source of food. They have been there every spring since I have been here, 1964 to the present. Pelican Lake is situated approximately 3 miles from Ouray Refuge.

H. J. Johnson, Manager, Ouray NWR

These two arid, treeless valleys (Rush and Cedar) lying to the west of Utah Lake support a high population of wintering bald eagles. This may be a recent phenomenon. R. G. Bee in 1960, made the first observation of 20 birds flying west at evening near the south end of Cedar Valley. By the winter of 1968-69, by actual count at the four night roosts, 119 bald eagles wintered in these two adjacent valleys, subsisting largely on blacktailed jackrabbits.

Clyde C. Edwards, PhD Thesis 1969, Brigham Young University

NEVADA:

Records over the last five years indicate an estimated 5 to 15 bald eagles use the Stillwater Area between mid-November and mid-March. Both adult and immature birds have been sighted.

Recent January aerial surveys of the entire Lahontan Valley estimate a wintering population of 20 to 30 bald eagles. There is some controversy as to whether this is the southern or northern subspecies.

Lynn C. Howard, Manager, Stillwater, NWR

No more than two bald eagles are observed using the refuge at any one time during the winter period.

R. V. Papike, Manager, Ruby Lake NWR

ARIZONA:

Although we winter only a few bald eagles, we did have an increase this year. Bald eagles were seen between December 4, 1976, and march 12, 1976. Five immature bald eagles were seen at one time in the vicinity of the refuge headquarters on March 9. Two and sometimes three eagles spent much of the day in the vicinity of a backwater lake by the refuge headquarters for a period of about four weeks. One had been seen catching and eating a small fish, presumably a bullhead catfish.

Mature bald eagles were seen on several occasions throughout the refuge (about 30 miles of river); however, it appeared that there were no more than three adults.

Gerald E. Duncan, Manager, Imperial NWR

BRITISH COLUMBIA:

We have not done extensive inventories of bald eagles in British Columbia, although a number of counts have been conducted in coastal areas incidental to other inventory work. These counts suggest that by far the greatest concentration of birds occur along the coast, where bald eagles both nest and winter in relatively large numbers. For instance, counts I conducted in the Queen Charlotte Islands provided indications of densities in the order of one to six birds per mile of coastline during the nesting season. It is my impression that densities are similar during the winter, although I have not completely worked up the data from winter counts.

I. D. Smith, Inventory Coordinator, Fish & Wildlife Branch, Department of Recreation & Conservation

PRAIRIE PROVINCES OF CANADA:

I know of no such overwintering aggregations of bald eagles in the prairie provinces of Canada. It is possible that they may occur in the East in the great lakes region.

Dr. W. J. Maher, University of Saskatchewan

WASHINGTON:

San Juan Island is a major wintering area for both adult and immature bald eagles and, to a much lesser degree, immature golden eagles.

Numbers vary from year to year, but in winter 1972-73 I recorded a peak of about 50 bald eagles on San Juan Island, concentrated mostly in the American Camp and San Juan Valley areas. Of these, about 40 were immatures. In winter 1973-74 I found a significant increase in numbers to about 75-80 for the island (25 in American Camp alone). This corresponded to record increases in the Skagit Valley, where the population is comprised mostly of adults. Winter 1974-75 and 1975-76 showed approximately the same high levels and proportions of adults to young.

William Stevens, National Park Service, San Juan Island

In the year that I've been here, I have not observed; nor do our records show any of the migratory influx of bald eagles during the fall-winter period that occurs in other areas such as Glacier National park. We have consistent year-round observations of bald eagles throughout the Recreation Area. These are usually only one or two birds at a time. It would be my guess that these are resident birds as some nests have been reported.

Roberta V. Seibel, Park Naturalist, Coulee Dam National Recreation Area

Records to 1965 show only an occasional sighting on Columbia National Wildlife Refuge.

James R. Good, Assistant Refuge Manager

Both bald and goldens arrive at Toppenish in November along with migrating waterfowl which it must be assumed that they move along with, though they lag somewhat. Waterfowl, mostly mallard, peak at 200,000 to 250,000 during November and January; balds at 4 to 8 and goldens at 6 to 12. Lesser Canadian Geese numbering (10,000 to 20,000) occur during January through April, and 2 to 6 balds work on them then move out. A few goldens are sighted into early June.

Conboy Lake waterfowl peaks at 15,000 to 20,000 in both spring and fall; balds at 1 to 2 and goldens 2 to 4 during these periods. Balds stay until early June, goldens until early July.

Larry LaRochelle, Manager, Toppenish & Conboy Lake NWR

Here along the coast we do not notice any buildups of eagles, nor do we note any increase of birds during migration periods. I have wondered why eagles do not concentrate along our area. The abundant fish runs and seabirds would afford them food and "easy living."

Joseph M. Welch, Manager, Willapa NWR

There are three dams located on the Skagit River within the Ross Lake National Recreation Area. We have as yet no appreciable concentrations of bald eagles below the tailwaters of the three dams. We do, on occasion, see a few eagles in these areas. The eagles start arriving on the Skagit River in November and peak out in numbers in December and January. Then they start decreasing in February and March.

John E. Jensen, District Manager, North Cascades National Park

On the Skagit River between Rockport and Newhalem, bald eagles in 1973-74 reached peak numbers of 93 on the 13 January, in 1974-75 the peak was 165 eagles on 12 February.

When salmon are plentiful in the early part of the winter, the eagles concentrate at areas where habitat conditions are optimal. As the season progresses and the concentrated salmon carcasses at favorable sites are depleted, the eagles' distribution changes, and the eagles be-

gin to disperse (spread out) along other stretches of the Skagit.
Christopher Servheen, MS Thesis, University of Washington (1975)

Turnbull hosts both bald and golden eagles during the period mid-November to mid-March. An estimated five bald eagles have used the area at one time usually during February. This year, however, several sightings occurred in April. Food source would probably be both open water fish areas and crippled waterfowl on the ice.
Maurice B. Wright, Assistant Manager, Turnbull NWR

I am enclosing a rough graph describing the population numbers on a 25-mile section of the Nooksack River. (A peak count of 105 bald eagles was recorded on January 22, 1976). This section supports about 95 percent of all eagles on the river. Similar results were obtained during the 1974-75 wintering season. I consider the counts to be a conservative estimate of the actual numbers.
Mark Stalmaster, Graduate Student, Huxley College of Environmental Studies

Quilcene Ranger District: Eight sightings this winter.
Hoodsport Ranger District: Ten to twenty sightings this winter, not at Forest proper, but at the mouth of Hamma Hamma River.
Quinault Ranger District: Ten to fifteen birds along upper Quinault River.
Fred Brandau, Wildlife Staff Officer, Olympic National Forest

We have observed 29 bald eagles wintering in groups of two to six birds along the Methow River between Carlton and Winthrop, Washington.
Irving E. Smith, Acting Former Supervisor, Okanogan National Forest

The biggest concentration of wintering bald eagles on or in the general vicinity of the Mt. Baker-Snoqualmie National Forest is on the Skagit River below the town of Marblemount. This is an estimated 150 birds. An area above Rockport has been established to preserve eagle wintering habitat. Five to ten birds drift onto the Forest up Bacon Creek, northeast of Marblemount, and 20 to 30 have been reported up the Cascade River, east of Marblemount. Several wintering eagles have also been seen at Baker Lake.

An estimated 100 wintering eagles have been reported west of the Forest on the North Fork Nooksack River. Some birds have been noted along the Sauk River up to the confluence of the White Chuck and up the Suiattle to All Creek, east of Darrington. An estimated 10 to 15 birds have been observed along the North Fork Stillaquamish River, especially around Ashton and Squire Creeks, west of Darrington.
Ed Wilder, Wildlife Specialist, Mt. Baker-Snoqualmie National Forest

Bald eagles have been sited at two locations on the Gifford Pinchot National Forest. Three pairs have been sited from time to time wintering on the Cowlitz River, west of Randle. An additional pair has been frequently sighted on Swift Reservoir. Nesting areas have not been located.

> *Paul R. Stenkamp, Wildlife Staff Officer, Gifford Pinchot National Forest*

OREGON:

A few pair frequent reservoirs and lakes of the Willamette Valley and Cascade Mountains, Lane County, Oregon. I must admit that I cannot account for any of the birds throughout a 12-month period, but I feel that one or two of the pairs are year-round residents.

Lookout Point Reservoir on the Middle Fork Willamette River is used by one pair and Waldo Lake another. Some long flights to food supply might be necessary for the Waldo Lake eagles during severe winter conditions. I am aware of a pair at Siltcoos Lake on the coast and would expect these to be year-round residents. I have no evidence that our coastal eagles move inward in winter. Eagles would have access to high waterfowl concentrations along the coast which would be more easily accessible than Klamath National Wildlife Refuge.

> *Robert N. Jubber, District Wildlife Biologist, Oregon State*

During the months of October through December, a concentration of adult and juvenile bald eagles builds up at Sheep Bridge and the head of Cultus River. Approximately 70 are the most that have been counted at one time. An average of 40 birds is the "normal" population during this period of time.

> *John C. Capp, Wildlife Staff Officer, Deschutes National Forest*

We have seen about 27 bald eagles this winter. Some of them, however, may be the same birds.

> *Chuck Sundstrom, Wildlife Staff Officer, Malheur National Forest*

Estimated numbers of bald eagles using and possibly perching on or near the Forest boundary on the east side is 15 to 20.

There appears to be a small number of birds ranging over and perching on the Clackamas Reservoir. As the food source is not plentiful or reliable, these birds should not be considered as permanent winter residents. I feel they spend most of their time on the lower Clackamas Reservoir, 4 to 10 miles west of the Forest boundary.

Estimated numbers of eagles using the Clackamas is three to seven. The Sandy River also supports a small number of birds. While these birds probably roost and feed mostly off Forest, they do make daily sojourns into the upper Sandy Reservoir area and Bull Run. The estimated number of eagles in this drainage is eight to twelve.

> *George H. Berscheid, Wildlife Staff Officer, Mt. Hood National Forest*

An estimate on numbers of wintering bald eagles for three different areas on or adjacent to the Ochoco National Forest are as follows:

1. Upper Crooked River drainage in the vicinity of Paulina, Oregon, 40 birds.

2. Lake Billy Chinook and Pelton Reservoir areas on the Deschutes River, 10 birds.

3. Crooked River drainage west of Prineville through to the Lake Billy Chinook, four birds.

Bernie Carter, Wildlife Staff Officer, Ochoco National Forest

The south half of the Umatilla lies adjacent to an important bald eagle wintering area. The total population is unknown; however, I am sure that this population numbers greater than 50 birds. Bald eagles are frequently sighted on the Forest. A pair of eagles are commonly sighted near Meadow Brook Summit on the Dale District. Small numbers are occasionally sighted near the North Fork of the John Day River on the Ukiah District. Bald eagles have been sighted on the Heppner District; however, sightings are extremely rare.

Roger E. Baker, Wildlife Staff Officer, Umatilla National Forest

Our best estimate would be between five and ten bald eagles on the Forest during the normal year.

Raymond Zalunardo, Wildlife Biologist, Umpqua National Forest

One definite (two probable) bald eagles observed several times in the Hereford area this winter. Also, one or two pairs observed in Township 12 South, Range 37 East, periodically throughout the year.

No known nests observed but believed because of the periodic year-round observations. There is probably at least one active bald eagle nest in the area.

Earl Fishburn, Resources Assistant, Unity Ranger District, Wallowa-Whitman National Forest

We are seeking and have been seeing eagles all winter at Hilgard State Park, La Grande Rifle Range on Highway 244 and Camp Elkana west of Starkey Flat. Never more than two at a time.

Doug Barton, Ranger, La Grande District, Wallowa-Whitman National Forest

There is only one bald eagle that district personnel have observed this winter. It has been seen up Catherine Creek about the state park. It has been seen there in previous winters, also.

Ray Randall, Resource Assistant, Union District, Wallowa-Whitman National Forest

We have an estimated population of ten eagles wintering on the Forest. There are four on or near Detroit Reservoir, two on or near Blue River and Cougar Reservoir and four on or near Hills Creek and Lookout Point Reservoir. We have two confirmed nests with one bringing off two young.

Ed Harshman, Wildlife Staff Officer, Willamette National Forest

The following information was collected and coordinated with Vic Coggins, biologist, OSF&WC, Enterprise and Ron Roheder, non-game biologist, OSF&WC, La Grande.

	Estimated Number
Wallowa County	
Snake River country	5
Wenaha River	10
Grande Ronde River	10
Wallowa River & Wallowa Valley	5
Minam River	5
Imnaha River	<u>3</u>
	38
Union County	
Powder River, Thief Valley	4
Starkey & Upper Grande Ronde	7
La Grande, Ladd Marsh	<u>6</u>
	17
Baker County	
Burnt River	4
Hell's Canyon, Brownlee & Oxbow Reservoirs	<u>26</u>
	30

These estimates do not take into account transients or annual and seasonal fluctuations.

Roy R. Sines, Ranger, Bear-Sleds District, Wallowa-Whitman National Forest

This winter the Fish & Wildlife Service eagle census in the Klamath Basin was taken on January 5. The survey route, approximately 140 miles long, covered the Sprague, Klamath, Lost and Sycan Rivers, Spring, Swan, and Klamath Lakes, and the refuge areas. Fifty-four adult and eight immature bald eagles were observed on the route. These areas are on or adjacent to the Forest. Large springs keep portions of the lakes and streams ice-free providing overwintering habitat.

A survey flown the same day over Tule, Clear, and Goose Lakes in northern California turned up 31 adults and four immatures.

Jack Inman, Wildlife Biologist, Winema National Forest

Bald eagles are only rarely observed on McNary Refuge lands and then appear to be transitory. Observations are usually of a single, mature bird in association with the Columbia River.

Owen R. Vivion, Manager, McNary NWR

The numbers of eagles usually peak during the month of January. On January 25, 1976, an effort was made to count the birds, and 18 adults and 7 young were observed. There could have been more young birds on the area at that time because in many cases long-range observations could not distinguish the young balds from the goldens.

A. Boyd Claggett, Manager, Summer Lake WMA, Oregon

During migration we usually see few eagles here; normally 2 to 6 per year.

John T. Annear, Manager, William L. Finley NWR

We have one pair resident bald eagles that nest near Lincoln city. From my limited observations, no eagles move in during the winter.

Jim Heintz, Oregon State Game Commission

In the past, 10 to 15 years ago, up to 10 bald eagles wintered at Cold Springs NWR and 1 or 2 were seen at McKay Creek NWR. We now see only an occasional bald eagle at either refuge. We suspect that they have moved to Umatilla Refuge because of the larger numbers of waterfowl and open water. (Cold Springs and McKay Creek occasionally freeze over, and waterfowl populations have dropped.)

On Umatilla NWR we normally expect a wintering population of from 7 to 13 bald eagles. In addition, there will be up to 10 golden eagles.

John E. Kurtz, Manager, Umatilla NWR

OREGON/CALIFORNIA:

Bald eagles on Klamath Basin NWR reach peak numbers varying from 12 to 176, ten-year average is 77. This is an overwintering population.

Robert C. Fields, Manager, Klamath Basin NWR

CALIFORNIA:

Most migrants stay in the northern tier of California counties. A few do make their way to southern California, however. We had nine bald eagles at Big Bear Lake outside of San Bernardino this past winter.

Jerry P. McIlwain, Leader, Threatened and Endangered Species Group, U.S. Forest Service

The winter of 1975-76 was exceptionally dry and warm on the Lassen, which may have allowed many bald eagles to stay on their summer range. Eagle Lake and McCoy Flat Reservoir had as many or more bald eagles during the winter. Honey Lake Valley had 10 to 20 bald eagles from December to February, all of which may have been migrants. I believe the main food source was dead livestock and deer based on reported sightings of bald eagles feeding. Waterfowl and fish are also major food items, and duck feathers, and fish bones were found under roost trees.

Gary Laver, Wildlife Biologist, Lassen National Forest

The bald eagle is rarely (at intervals of two to five years) observed during the winter on the San Francisco Bay National Wildlife Refuge.

No bald eagles have been recorded on the Farallon Islands or recently recorded on the San Pablo Bay National Wildlife Refuge.

Robert G. Personius, Manager, San Francisco Bay NWR

The Kern or Pixley refuges do not winter any bald eagles nor do they nest in this part of California's Southern San Joaquin Valley. Refuge records since 1970 only show 7 use days in January of 1972. I have talked with several state and federal officers, and they said it is rare to

see bald eagles, (once every 3 to 5 years).
Thomas J. Charmley, Manager, Kern-Pixley NWR

The two Havasu sightings, other than the nesting pair, are only on the refuge for a few days. They were seen in early to mid-December.
Robert L. Delaney, Manager, Havasu NWR

Researching the narrative reports on the San Luis National Wildlife Refuge Complex, there were two reported incidents of bald eagles. The first involved a mature bald eagle sighted off and on for a week during December, 1973. The second case also involved a mature bird seen once in mid-November, 1975.
Leon A. Littlefield, Manager, San Luis NWR Complex

On our bird list we show bald eagles as being rare winter visitors, and I believe this is a fair general statement of their presence here.
Jack Helvie, Manager, Sacramento NWR

Bald eagles, numbers given parenthetically, were reported on the following years: 43 (1), 46 (3), 49 (4), 50 (4), 51 (1), 52 (4), 53 (5), 54 (4), 55 (2), 56 (4), 59 (1), 70 (1), 71 (1), 73 (5), 74 (3), 75 (6). A Christmas count has been made each year since 1940, but the numbers of observers and thoroughness of the coverage has been quite variable.

The absence of eagles on the counts for the years 1960 through 1969 is probably due to the way Big Bear Lake was managed. As I recall fairly adequate water levels were maintained in the early 50's (and presumably in the late 40's). Low rainfall and increasing use of the water for domestic uses and irrigation caused the water level to fall; and by the early 60's there was usually very little water in the lake when the Christmas counts were made. Then through agreements among the various agencies that control water in California, the water company in the Redlands area received compensatory water and, as a result, the water level in Big Bear Lake was restored about 10 years ago. The lake is now used primarily for recreation.
Leo R. Best, Mt. San Antonio College, Walnut, California

I am not certain which subspecies of bald eagle we are dealing with at Salton Sea NWR, but assume they are probably the southern subspecies. We usually see only immature eagles and only from October through January and not always each year.
Don V. Tiller, Asst. Mgr., Salton Sea NWR

We find no record of bald eagles wintering on Humboldt Bay. There are several populations recognized that winter a few to many miles inland in the north coast counties.
Larry H. Worden, Mgr., Humboldt Bay NWR

A wintering area supporting from 10 to 30 bald eagles is located on the Papoose Arm of Clair Engle Lake, Trinity County. These birds include some residents and are feeding on spawning Kokanee salmon.

A wintering population, ranging from 1-12 bald eagles use the Tuolumne River near La Grange, California. Numbers appear to be correlated with the king salmon runs.
Robert D. Mallette, Assoc. Wildlife Mgr-Biol., Calif. State

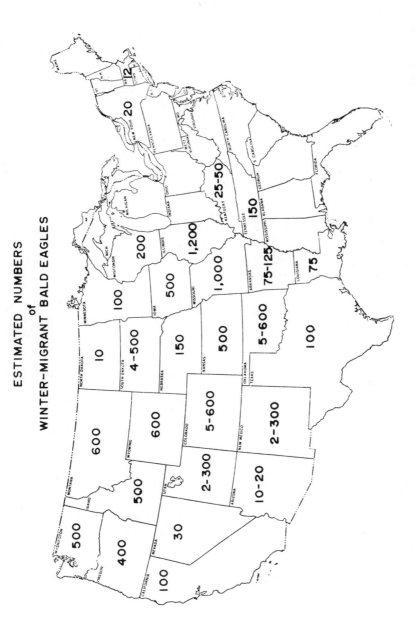

ESTIMATED NUMBERS
of
WINTER-MIGRANT BALD EAGLES

D. A. SPENCER 1976

2
Mid-winter Waterfowl
Bald Eagle Inventories

The number of migrant bald eagles that winter in the lower 48 states each year must remain a debatable figure until our inventory methods are both expanded and improved. Based on the best estimates now available, a reasonable figure is some 8-9,000 birds. This figure excludes the resident populations in Maine, in the Chesapeake Bay area, Florida, along the coasts of Louisiana and Texas, and in southcentral Arizona—all of which are resident and (with the exception of Maine) nesting. The coastal populations of British Columbia, Alaska, and a few in the Maritimes, totaling an estimated 50,000 birds which are essentially non-migratory, must be included in the total North American population.

The figure of 8-9,000 migrant bald eagles is much higher than is indicated by any of the field inventories, yet may be well under the actual numbers present. For example, the mid-winter waterfowl inventories conducted by State Game Agencies and coordinated by the U.S. Fish and Wildlife Service, cover by air all major waterfowl congregating areas during the first week of January. In the last several years, bald and golden eagles have been added to the records being taken on these one-day inventories. In January 1976 this inventory recorded 3,785 bald eagles in the western U.S. under discussion here. But weather just prior to these one-day counts, together with the fact that bald eagles are not exclusively associated with waterfowl, makes such an approach to total population quite inadequate. For example, the mid-winter inventory in Colorado recorded only 57 birds, while more intensive surveys that same season estimated that between 500 and 600 bald eagles were present in the state. The mid-winter waterfowl inventory in Illinois covered the Illinois River and that part of the Mississippi River north of the junction of the two. Important segments south of this triangle were unreported. Thus increasing the actual count of 895 eagles to an estimated 1,200 in the state as a whole is not out of reason.

In January 1972 and 1973, the state of Wyoming conducted an aerial count of eagles based on randomly established, 50 mile-long transects. They flew 5,450 miles of transects in 1972 and 6,300 miles in 1973. The 1972 results were so much higher than anyone anticipated that the National Audubon Society joined in the project in 1973—a year in which an estimated 600 plus bald eagles were recorded. The mid-winter waterfowl inventory in Wyoming does not even approach this coverage, and in January 1976 reported only 132 bald eagles.

The above are not isolated comparisons but can be repeated in the majority of states.

The Audubon Christmas Bird Count is another nationwide program that provides some insight into the wintering populations of bald eagles. Since the 15-mile diameter count circles are not positioned with any one bird species in mind, they cannot be expected to serve as a census of numbers. On the other hand, these records are very valuable in extending our knowledge of where bald eagles are wintering. Members of local chapters, with season-long observation opportunities, have made important contributions to this source paper.

In December 1974 (the most recent compilation available at press time), 155 of the 506 counts (30 percent) made in western states recorded one or more bald eagles. The 1,338 bald eagles sighted on this one-day field study is not a bad record when the limited area coverage is taken into account.

Just as a matter of interest: Nine of the eleven (81 percent) Audubon Christmas Bird Counts in Alaska reported bald eagles. The 15-mile diameter circle of the Klukwan Audubon Club held 1,162 bald eagles!

For 16 years or better Elton Fawks, under the auspices of the National Audubon Society, has organized and directed a special one-day count of wintering bald eagles in the upper Mississippi River drainage. He enlists local Audubon clubs, federal and state game biologists, lock masters, and other dedicated birders, often totaling in the neighborhood of 500 participants. On a selected day in February, on foot, and by car, boat or plane, they cover the Mississippi River from south of St. Louis on north, and the Illinois, Wisconsin, and portions of the Ohio and Missouri Rivers. Progressively, off-side wildlife refuges have been included in the coverage. In 1977 the National Wildlife Federation, under a grant from the Exxon Corporation, is asking Elton Fawks to extend this study nationwide. In 1976 there was an early break-up of ice so that the annual count on February 14th missed the peak in regional numbers, yet totaled 1,012 bald eagles.

In the records of bald eagle numbers kept by resident managers of federal and state wildlife management areas lie some of the most informative data available. There are many locations about the United States where weekly counts have been made each winter, from the arrival of the first eagle in the fall to the last straggler to head back north in the spring. Best of all, accompanying information on prey species and abundance, on weather, on icing conditions and snow cover, and other factors influencing the day to day variation in numbers of eagles present, is often available to interpret what would otherwise be an exercise in figures. For example, on Muleshoe National Wildlife Refuge in the panhandle of Texas, from 1968 through 1975, days-of-eagle-use of the refuge varied as follows: 125-145-20-25-355-616-63-35. The records show that the playa lakes that attract waterfowl, upon which bald eagles are preying, dried-up in 1970 and 1971, and again in 1974 and 1975 from regionwide drought. Both waterfowl and bald eagles accordingly shifted wintering base those years.

Particularly gratifying was learning how observant were resident personnel on ranger districts of the national forests. Many overwintering locations of bald eagles in the Pacific Northwest would have been omitted from this source paper without their contributions. Not seeking the same participation of all nine National Forest Regions was a regrettable error on the part of this editor.

MID-WINTER WATERFOWL/BALD EAGLE INVENTORY
NATIONAL SUMMARY

State	Bald Eagles *1975	1976	State	Bald Eagles 1975	1976**
Alabama	1	2	Nebraska	125	105
Arizona	2	–	Nevada	7	40
Arkansas	96	44	New Jersey	–	5
California	74	17	New Mexico	36	47
Colorado	74	57	New York	–	2
Delaware	–	3	North Carolina	2	–
Florida	28	46	North Dakota	9	7
Idaho	91	91	Ohio	8	4
Illinois	498	764	Oklahoma	197	63
Indiana	3	1	Oregon	64	62
Iowa	54	230	Pennsylvania	1	2
Kansas	92	205	South Carolina	17	16
Kentucky	44	31	South Dakota	249	366
Louisiana	5	–	Tennessee	130	94
Maine	12	4	Texas	65	19
Maryland	10	17	Utah	48	90
Michigan	2	0	Virginia	–	10
Minnesota	19	68	Washington	308	321
Mississippi	1	1	Wisconsin	10	81
Missouri	473	529	Wyoming	37	132
Montana	174	209			
U.S. Total (1975)	3,066		U.S. Total (1976)		3,785

*Omits 75 Unidentified Eagles
**Omits 143 Unidentified Eagles

Data: Courtesy U.S. Fish & Wildlife Service, Migratory Bird Management.

BALD EAGLES RECORDED DURING STATE AND FEDERAL MID-WINTER WATERFOWL INVENTORY

Year	Washington	Oregon	Idaho	Nevada	California	Regional Totals
1964	73	59	34	18	56	240
1965	134	46	55	3	85	323
1966	45	52	61	5	28	191
1967	59	135	91	4	41	330
1968	156	109	76	6	161	508
1969	127	61	34	11	19	252
1970	110	102	59	5	81	357
1971	142	66	91	7	84	390
1972	298	79	105	13	50	536
1973	308	64	91	7	84	554
1974	321	62	91	40	17	531
1975	271	59	144	39	13	526
1976	299	90	255	30	73	747

Data: Courtesy Migratory Bird Management U.S.D.I.: Fish and Wildlife Service

AUDUBON WINTER BALD EAGLE COUNT (FEBRUARY)

Year	Lock & Dam 3 to 11	Mississippi River Lock & Dam 12 to 22	Lock & Dam To Below St. Louis	Illinois River	Bald Eagles
1971	154	365	120	78	717
1972	286	456	151	254	1,147
1973	147	445	139	142	873
1974	182	375	72	69	698
1975	258	346	124	284	1,012
1976	325	289	169	229	1,012

Coordinated by Elton Fawks

Participation may involve as many as 500 cooperators including state and federal wildlife biologists, refuge managers, lock masters, and local Audubon clubs. The inventory is a complex of sighting methods: aircraft, boat, automobile, and foot. Coverage has been progressively expanded and improved, but as with all one-day counts, the weather is an uncontrolled variable that aggregates or disperses the population making fixed-point observation station results quite variable. —Editor

NEW MEXICO:

Last spring I put together a rough compilation of the eagle records between November and March and came to the conclusion that at least two hundred and probably 300 or more bald eagles were present in New Mexico during that period.

John Hubbard, Project Leader, Endangered Species Program, New Mexico Department of Game & Fish

ILLINOIS:

Survey results—as determined from waterfowl flights during the first week of January since 1971.

Location	1971	1972	1973	1974	1975	1976
Upper Illinois River	0	4	40	35	42	100
Lower Illinois River	9	13	92	78	143	208
Upper Mississippi River	14	40	64	151	192	143
Dubuque to Rock Island (Jan. 9, 1976)						177
Lower Mississippi River	117	38	322	268	177	267
Total	140	95	518	532	554	895

MID-WINTER 1976 WATERFOWL/EAGLE INVENTORY

Aerial Survey Area	December 16	January 5	March 2
Upper Illinois River	69	100	—
Lower Illinois River	141	208	—
Lower Mississippi River	137	267	43
Upper Mississippi River	102	143	=

Note: The above one-day flights cover the Illinois River and its associated oxbow lakes and marshlands from Peru, Illinois, on the north to the junction with the Mississippi on the south: the Mississippi River from a short distance above St. Louis north to Moline, Illinois. Other important sectors of the Mississippi River for bald eagles are not included nor are off-river eagle wintering areas.

State of Illinois: Department of Conservation

LOUISIANA:

If I had to estimate the number of wintering birds (northern bald eagles) in Louisiana during an average year, it would be between 50 to 75 individuals, with this figure reaching 100 during some severe winters.

S. Ray Aycock, Jr., Wildlife Management Biologist, U.S. Fish and Wildlife Service

SOUTH DAKOTA:

The only detailed information we have on numbers of eagles in South Dakota is that information derived from our mid-winter waterfowl survey. Listed below is a table showing the breakdown in the eagle populations during the mid-winter survey for the period of 1970-1976:

Year	Unknown	Bald	Golden	Total
1970	33	86	49	168
1971	31	141	97	269
1972	29	178	106	313
1973	52	249	169	470
1974	51	366	213	630
1975	12	309	239	558
1976	28	302	137	467

The eagle concentration areas during the winter months are in the vicinity of the tailwaters of the Oahe Reservoir, Lake Sharpe Reservoir, Lake Francis Case Reservoir, and Clark Reservoir. Of these four areas the latter two would have the greatest concentrations.

Warren Jackson, Director, South Dakota Division of Game & Fish

WASHINGTON:

The mid-winter eagle inventory was conducted from January 5-16, 1976, and a total of 299 bald eagles were counted.

Carroll A. Rieck, Superintendent, Non Game Program, Washington State Department of Game

MICHIGAN:

According to Edward Mikula, waterfowl specialist, no eagles were recorded during the mid-winter waterfowl census.

Victor S. Janson, Department of Natural Resources, Wildlife Division

IDAHO:

The aerial survey from Coeur d'Alene Lake north to the Canadian Border only recorded 119 bald eagles on January 5th. This being a one-shot venture, we surely missed some birds, but we did identify concentration areas and obtained a feeling for total numbers. Based on the flight and other observations throughout the winter, I feel it is quite reasonable to state that there is a wintering population of some 200 bald eagles distributed from the St. Joe River north to the Canadian Border.

Joseph B. Lint, Wildlife Biologist, Bureau of Land Management, Coeur d'Alene (Participated in Aerial Inventory)

MID-WINTER (JANUARY 5-9)
WATERFOWL/EAGLE INVENTORY

Wintering Numbers Along The Snake River (Counted)

Location	Bald Eagles
Island Park: North Fork	9
St. Anthony (City)	3
South Fork of the Snake	15
Roberts Area	7
American Falls to Shelley	18
American Falls near Bottoms	31
Snake River below American Falls	7
Lake Walcott	1
Lower Snake River—Brownlee Dam on	45
Burley Area	2
Twin Falls Area	3
Hagerman Area	2
C. J. Strike Reservoir	5
Walters Ferry to Farewell Bend	7
Payette River	4
Boise River	4
Deer Flat Refuge	18
Pend Oreille Lake	64
Pend Oreille River	22
Coeur d'Alene Lake	33

Other Over-wintering Sites In Idaho (Estimated)

Location	Bald Eagles
Upper Salmon River	15
Clearwater River—Dworshak Dam	10-12
to Lewiston	10-12
Lochsa—Selway Rivers	8
Middle Fork Boise River	25
South Fork—Boise River	12
South Fork—Payette River	6-8
Middle Fork—Salmon River	8
Total of both categories	388

Dick Norell, Game Bird Superintendent, Idaho Fish & Fame Department

ARKANSAS:

The count is carried out jointly by the U.S. Fish and Wildlife Service and personnel with the commission. Conducted January 5-9, the survey showed a total of 46 adult and 20 immature bald eagles. Thurman Booth, with the Fish & Wildlife Service in Little Rock, reports that the annual survey figures have ranged from 9 to 116 over the past fourteen years since the counts were initiated. Wintering locations in Arkansas as of January 5-9, 1976:

Location	Bald Eagles
White River NWR & vicinity	2
Lake Norfork	18
Bull Shoals Lake	14
Lake Ouachita	17
Bois d'Arc Lake	1
Millwood Reservoir & vicinity	4
Big Lake NWR	2
Harris Brake Lake	1
Holla Bend NWR & Arkansas River	12
Eleven-Point River	1
Push Mountain Road	1
Old River	1
Pullen Pond	1

Brad Kennedy, Information Specialist, in Arkansas Outdoors, Arkansas Game & Fish Commission

NORTH DAKOTA:

During the mid-winter waterfowl survey, we cover the Missouri River, Yellowstone River, and a few other creeks that have open water. The coverage is an aerial survey in early January.

Year	Bald Eagles	Year	Bald Eagles
1960	0	1969	1
1961	2	1970	3
1962	0	1971	2
1963	3	1972	4
1964	5	1973	4
1965	4	1974	4
1966	8	1975	12
1967	5	1976	9
1968	2		

C. Schroeder, Superintendent, Migratory Game Bird Management, North Dakota Game & Fish Department

WYOMING:

State aircraft flew 5,450 miles of transects in 1972 and 6,300 miles in 1973. Of the 272 randomly selected transects to be covered, only 109 were flown in 1972 and 126 completed in 1973. Good weather was the prime ingredient for flying the census lines, and high winds and storms proved to be the biggest handicap in the winter censuses.

Because they were somewhat skeptical of the results of the 1972 eagle census, especially since the figures were much larger than even the highest previous estimates, the National Audubon Society sent its own team of observers to participate in the 1973 eagle count. After flying their own transect lines simultaneously with the Game and Fish counts, the Audubon personnel expressed to Wrakestraw their satisfaction and confidence in his survey methods.

The census in 1973 revealed a total estimated eagle population in Wyoming of 10,554, including 9,046 golden, 618 bald and 890 unidentified eagles.

Larry Roop, Wyoming Wildlife 37 (6): page 18, June 1973.

See also: The 1973 Wyoming Bald and Golden Eagle Survey. George F. Wrakestraw, American Birds, August 1973, pages 716-718.

COLORADO:

Ervin Boeker of the U.S. Fish and Wildlife Service in Denver; Eugene Knoder, Audubon Society, Denver; and Jerry Craig, Raptor Biologist, Colorado Division of Wildlife, flew aerial transects of the San Luis Valley during the week of January 30, this year (1976), and from these transects it was estimated that between 200 and 250 bald eagles were in the valley at that time.

Charles R. Bryant, Refuge Mgr., Monte Vista NWR

Our estimate of total bald eagles wintering in Colorado varies from 500 to 600 individuals. They are concentrated primarily along the major river systems (the Colorado, South Platte, Arkansas, Dolores, Rio Grande and Gunnison Rivers) where they feed upon crippled waterfowl. They are also dependent upon winter killed elk and deer and frequent such carcasses throughout the winter.

Early in the winter (late November and early December) concentrations of bald eagles frequent the large reservoirs in eastern Colorado. Most frequented reservoirs are Bonny, Jumbo, Jackson, Sterling, and Riverside.

Gerald R. Craig, Raptor Biologist, Colorado Division of Wildlife

3
Audubon Christmas Bird Count–
Western States

75th Audubon Christmas Bald Eagle Count (December 1974)
From: American Birds 29 (2): April 1975

Louisiana (12)
Natchitoches—1
Shreveport—1
Venice—1

Arkansas (16)
Arkadelphia—1
Holla Bend NWR—6
Lake Georgia-Pacific—5
Lake Millwood—8
Pine Bluff—1
White River NWR—1

Texas (59)
Amarillo—5
Buffalo Lake NWR—1
Lake Meredith (East)—2
Lake Meredith (West)—13
Lake O' the Pines—5
Midland—1
Muleshow NWR—2
Nacogdoches—2
Orange—2
Palo Pinto—5
Sherman—2
Trinidad—2

Oklahoma (16)
Arnett—1
Broken Bow Reservoir—2
Gibson Reservoir—15
Hula Reservoir—1
Kenton/Black Mesa—3
Salt Plains NWR—13
Sequoyah NWR—16
Spavinaw—3
Wichita Mountain NWR—8

Kansas (20)
Elk City Reservoir—2
Great Bend—5
Junction City—1
Kingman WMA—2
Lawrence—2
Linn County—9
Manhattan—26
Quivira NWR—31
Wichita—1

Kentucky (12)
Land Between Lakes—9

Tennessee (18)
Knox County—1
Norris—1
Reelfoot Lake—39

Missouri (17)
Hannibal—8
Mingo NWR—28
Montrose Lake WMA—2
Squaw Creek NWR—89
Sullivan—1

Illinois (37)
Beverly—3
Bloomington—1
Centralia—1
Chautauqua NWR—11
Chillicothe—1
Crab Orchard NWR—22
Crane Lake/Sangamon—10
Horseshoe Lake—48
Pere Marquette State Park—76
Quincy—35
Union County—15
West Mercer County—37

Iowa (16)
Burlington—20
Clinton—21
Davenport—8
Dubuque—35
Muscatine—34
Princeton/Camanche—55
Shenandoah—2
Sioux City—1
Yellow River Forest—11

Wisconsin (37)
Augusta—3
Beetown—25
Dancy—1
Grantsburg—1
Green Bay—1
La Crosse—4
Nelson—23
New Richmond—2
Poynette—1

Nebraska (5)
Scottsbluff—6

North Dakota (12)
Bismarck—1

South Dakota (11)
Hot Springs—4
Lake Andes—14
Piere—15
Yankton—7

Minnesota (31)
Afton—1
Duluth—2
Excelsior—1
Hasting—12
Saint Paul (Northeast)—1
Sherburne NWR—1
Wabasha—42
Winona—3

Wyoming (10)
Casper—13
Dubois—5
Jackson Hole—12
Lander—1
Seedskadee NWR—1
Sheridan—1
Story/Big Horn—6

Colorado (20)
Bonny Reservoir—4
Boulder—1
Denver (Jefferson County)—1
Durango (Pastorius Reservoir)—9
Fort Collins—2
Hotchkiss—1
Longmont (River Flood Plain)—3
Monte Vista NWR—26
Nunn—1
Pikes Peak—1
Weldona/Fort Morgan—1

New Mexico (14)
Clayton—2
Espanola—1
Glenwood—1
Las Vegas—3

Montana (8)
Big Fork—18
Billings—11
Ennis—5
Helena—3
Missoula—1
Park County—1

Idaho (11)
American Falls Reservoir—1
Indian Mountain—1
Nampa—35
Rupert—1
Salmon—2

Utah (7)
Bear River MBR—38
Clear Lake—4
Duchesne—2
Hyde Park—1
Provo—2
Salt Lake—4

Arizona (13)
Martinez Lake Yuma—2

Nevada (6)
None

Alaska (11)
Adak—143
Cordova—116
Glacier Bay—50
Homer—5
Izembek Northwest Range—4
Ketchikan—21
Klukwan—1,162
Kodiak—104
Sitka—30

British Columbia (17)
Chilliwack—46
Duncan—11
Kitimat—21
Ladner—3
Nanaimo—41
Pender Islands—18
Sayward—3
Terrace—4

Vancouver—8
Vaseux Lake—1
Victoria—24
White Rock—1

Washington (14)
Bellingham—7
Everett—1
Kitsap County—1
Padilla Bay—8
San Juan Island—6
Spokane—1
Tacoma—4
Wenatchee—1

Oregon (20)
Bend—2
Coos Bay—3
Cottage Grove—1
Eugene—1
Malheur NWR—4
Oak Ridge—4
Portland—1
Sauvie Island—3

California (64)
Big Bear Lake—3
Contra Costa County—1
Crystal Springs Reservoir—2
Del Norte County—1
Honey Lake—9
Idyllwild—2
Lewiston—21
Lost Lake/Fresno—6
Oakland—1
Oroville—2
Putah Creek—2
Springville—3
Woodfords—2

Total Number of Count Circles—506
  (Omitting Alaska and British Columbia)
Count Circles Recording Bald Eagles—155
Percent of Circles Recording Bald Eagles—30.6
Total Number of Wintering Bald Eagles
  Sighted in December 1974—1,338

4

Arrival and Departure of Migrant Bald Eagles

The arrival of northern migrant bald eagles each fall depends, after a nudge from impending winter, on how "the table is set." From the interior of Canada, the bald eagles for the most part are accompanying the southward movement of waterfowl upon which they are preying. Since waterfowl have numerous "way-stations" where they may pause for weeks to feed before proceeding on south, some eagles follow suit. Thus, from October to early December, a stepwise flight southward can be demonstrated.

On the other hand, independent of waterfowl movement, bald eagles may head directly for a regularly occurring source of fish—such as a spawning run. Arrival is dictated by the onset of spawning and departure from the area on when the supply of spawned-out fish is exhausted. In mid-November there were 377 bald eagles along McDonald Creek in Montana feeding on Kokanee salmon, and a month later the area was virtually deserted. By recording the number of eagles present at weekly intervals (as is the practice of many state and federal Wildlife Refuges), a pattern of eagle movements within a region is possible; and factors affecting this transfer can be assessed.

In addition, there are hundreds of sites where an almost continual supply of fish, such as carp, are crowded into shallow water during low-flow periods in the fall; and fish stunned in passing through the turbines at hydroelectric dams. So many southern wintering sites, like Reelfoot Lake in Tennessee and Salt Plains National Wildlife Refuge in Oklahoma, may begin to record bald eagles almost as soon as the more northern wintering grounds. In other words, there is some through-traffic.

There can be much shifting about in the period from mid-December to mid-February; but the birds involved, with rare exception, are those of a particular geographic locality. Thus, nearly every reservoir in Kansas is the realm of a state-based wintering population of bald eagles that change lakes and streams as weather and food availability dictate.

MONTANA:

The first arrivals may be expected around the last week in September. Most rapid buildup in numbers takes place during the last week of October and the first two weeks in November, with the peak count occurring on November 16 as an average. Numbers drop off sharply after the peak. Departure of the birds is closely correlated to the availability of salmon, and to weather conditions to a lesser degree. By the middle of December, nearly all eagles have left the study area and are dispersed down the Flathead River.

David S. Shea, McDonald Creek, Glacier National Park

The earliest fall record is November 5. . . normally the species does not arrive until about November 20. Rather than exhibiting a fall peak, the species appear to build up gradually in numbers through the winter, reaching maximum abundance at the time of the major break-up of ice at Ennis Lake, about April 1.

From: "Birds of the Bozeman Latilong (1969)" by P. D. Skaar at Ennis Lake

Bald eagles arrive along the Yellowstone River at Billings, Montana, every year about the 15th of December or perhaps a week earlier and leave around March 15th. The numbers vary as shown in the Christmas Bird Count. 1970 (10), 1971 (11), 1972 (16), 1973 (5), and 1974 (11).

Don MacDonald, Billings, Montana, Audubon Society

Bald eagles first arrive in eastern Montana on and around November 5. Departure dates for this species have been as late as March 27.

When observing the migration of these birds, the following seems to hold true—in the fall the bald eagles first to arrive are found along waterways but eventually disperse into other habitat types like ponderosa pine and big sage stands. In the spring there appears to be almost a mirror image, those occupying ponderosa pine, sage, etc., leave first. Those along waterways are the last to leave.

Terrence P. McEneaney, Biologist Technician, U.S. Fish & Wildlife Service, Sheridan, Wyoming

Bald eagles here in the valley are most numerous from about November to early April. Sightings are seldom made during summer and early fall (May to October), but at least one pair nests within 17 miles of Helena. This is in the area known as the "Gates of the Mountains."

Mrs. William F. McKinney, Helena, Montana, Audubon Society

NORTH DAKOTA:

Fall migration typically follows the pattern of the 1975 observations. The first bald eagle was reported at Upper Souris National Wildlife Refuge on October 1. Scattered reports of bald eagles were received until about November 20. In most years, bald eagles seem to move through North Dakota in mid-November with few reports in December.

During the spring migration, the first bald eagle is usually seen in early or mid-March, with peak numbers observed in the first one-third of April. Few are observed after April 15.

W. Reid Goforth, Director, Northern Prairie Wildlife Research Center, U.S. Fish & Wildlife Service

Spring migrants are generally sighted during the last two weeks in March, and fall migrants first seen in early November. In most years from three to seven bald eagles are sighted in both spring and fall migrations. The birds seem to stay for only a short period although available food due to waterfowl migrations seems to be unlimited.

Jon M. Malcolm, Manager, J. Clark Salyer NWR

SOUTH DAKOTA:

At the Sand lake NWR we observe from six to twelve bald eagles in both the spring and fall and an occasional one during the summer or winter. In the spring the birds pretty much are just passing through and only stay for a short time. They usually start showing up mid to late March along with the spring migration of waterfowl and other birds.

In the fall the eagles again start showing up with the return migration of waterfowl (around the first of October). They usually stay through the hunting season feeding on crippled ducks and geese. Usually the eagles will be gone by mid-December but sometimes stay on into January if we still have cripples around.

William C. Blair, Manager, Sand Lake NWR, Columbia, South Dakota

The migrations of bald eagles in South Dakota pretty much follows the migration of the waterfowl. They usually begin arriving during the month of October and by the end of November have reached substantial numbers. They reach a peak sometime during the months of December and January. The overwintering population departs in the springtime about the time of the first northward migration of waterfowl which would be early in March.

Warren Jackson, Director, South Dakota Division of Game & Fish

NEBRASKA:

The eagles arrive at the sanctuary in early January and stay until about the last week in march. They are migratory through the sanctuary, but we do have birds that stay during this period.

Robert J. Wicht, Manager, Lillian Annette Rowe, Audubon Wildlife Sanctuary

MINNESOTA:

Very few bald eagles are observed from January-March, and the first spring migrants usually start showing up about the first week in March and peak around the second week in April. Most of the eagles stop over for a few days to a week and then move on.

The main migrational periods are in March and April in the spring and from September through December in the fall.

John E. Wilbrecht, Manager, Sherburne NWR

Movement into the area coincides with the buildup of waterfowl populations. Peak eagle numbers can be expected in mid to late October. Most years eagles will depart shortly after freeze-up in November. The spring population peak is normally fewer than five birds.

Joseph Kotok, Manager, Agassiz NWR

WISCONSIN:

Bald eagles usually begin arriving on the Cassville District of the Upper Mississippi River Wildlife and Fish Refuge in early November, depending on weather conditions. This season the first bald eagle was sighted on November 1, 1975.

Eagles are usually on the District through late March or early April. Last year they stayed later than usual with the last eagle seen on April 26, 1975.

Robert E. Wilson, Manager, Cassville District, Upper Mississippi River NWR

The Winona (Trempealeau) District of the Upper Mississippi River Wildlife and Fish Refuge does host numbers of migrating and wintering eagles. Reports of bald eagles generally run from mid-September through early May. Peak migration periods are mid to late November and mid-March.

Hilma L. Volk, Assistant Manager, Winona District, Upper Mississippi River NWR

At Necedah the fall eagle migration starts with sightings of immature bald eagles from early to mid-September. Bald eagles peak in mid-October. The period is usually the peak in waterfowl numbers also.

Bald eagles are occasionally noted on the refuge in January and early February on nice days. These birds are usually adult birds and are presumably birds from the Petenwell dam area enjoying a warm day. In late February and early March, immature birds start showing up again but nowhere in the numbers noted in the fall. The eagles are mostly gone by the third week in March and are not noted until the immatures start arriving again in early September.

Dennis W. Strom, Manager, Necedah NWR

ILLINOIS:

The first observation in 1975 of a bald eagle on the Louisa District of the Mark Twain NWR was October 18th. The year before (1974) the last bird was observed on March 26th. Arrival at the Keithsburg Division is somewhat later each fall—on November 19, 1975. Over the past ten years in which records have been kept, the last few bald eagles were still around in mid-April.

> *Tom J. Early, District Manager, Mark Twain NWR*

The first bald eagles usually appear on these divisions around the last week in October or the first week in November and all are usually departed by mid-March.

> *Hugh H. Null, District Manager, Mark Twain NWR, Swan and Gilbert Lakes: Illinois River*

Bald eagles usually arrive on the Savanna District of the Upper Mississippi River NWR sometime in September. The population slowly builds to a peak which occurs during January or February depending upon weather conditions. During the spring the eagles usually have left the district during late March or early April. On a few occasions eagles have been observed during May and June, but these sightings are few and considered unusual.

> *Thomas D. Atkins, District Manager, Upper Mississippi River NWR, Savanna District*

By the time the annual Eagle Count sponsored by Elton Fawks and the Illinois Audubon Society was conducted—always scheduled for the weekend in the middle of February—the weather had warmed, the rivers had thawed much more than usual, and the birds had begun their northward migration much earlier than usual.

> *James M. Lockart, Supervisor, Division of Wildlife Resoruces, Illinois Department of Conservation*

MISSOURI:

Bald eagles normally stay at Squaw Creek from late September-early October until mid-April. Eagle numbers normally peak in December or early January.

> *Gerald M. Nugent, Manager, Squaw Creek NWR*

Mingo National Wildlife Refuge hosts a wintering bald eagle population during the time period October through March. These birds normally start arriving during October, peak during December through January, and depart by March.

> *Gerald L. Clawson, Manager, Mingo NWR*

Bald eagles generally begin showing up about mid-October on the Fountain Grove Wildlife Area. Their population usually peaks in mid-December or early January.

> *Robert Dobbins, Manager, Fountain Grove WMA, Missouri*

MISSOURI RIVER IMPOUNDMENTS:

The months of highest concentrations of eagles varied as follows:

1. Lewis and Clark Lake, Lake Oahe, and Lake Sakakawea report January as the peak month.

2. Lake Francis Case and Lake Sharpe report December as peak month.

3. Fort Peck Lake reports November or December as peak month, depending on weather conditions to the north of Montana.

Russel L. Bywater, Omaha District, Corps of Engieners, U.S. Army

KANSAS:

Lake McKinney will usually winter 100,000 mixed ducks (90 percent mallards) and 500 to 1,000 geese in a good year *when the lake has water.*

The eagles usually show up in late October or November about the time ducks arrive. I usually notice more eagles in December or January when the lake may freeze nearly closed. The eagles will then be seen sitting on ice near open water or near resting waterfowl.

Bruce C. Peters, District Game Protector, Southwest Kansas

Eagle population begins to peak in mid-December with the peak of the mallard population and the close of the local waterfowl hunting season. The eagles are apparently attracted by the concentration of crippled birds.

The small water units may freeze quickly in early December and remain frozen. There may be very little open water for several weeks during extended severe cold periods. The mallards, geese, and eagles sit around on the ice of the Little Marsh. If snow cover is sufficient to cover the waterfowl food supply, waterfowl and most of the eagles leave the area until a warm-up occurs.

Charles R. Darling, Manager, Quivira NWR

Kirwin Refuge normally has wintering bald eagles from about the first of December through the end of February. The peak is usually reached about the first of the year and remains rather constant until the birds leave.

Keith S. Hansen, Manager, Kirwin NWR

OKLAHOMA:

Eagles usually begin showing up along with our fall arrival of geese in late October and a few remain into late March.

Bill Hawthorne, Assistant Manager, Tishomingo NWR

Bald eagles arrive annually at the Wichita during November. Their numbers usually peak in late December or early January. It is my observation that our wintering population of bald eagles depends on the severity of the winter; fewer eagles during an open winter, and more eagle during period of freeze-ups.

Gene Bartnicki, Wildlife Biologist, Wichita Mountains NWR

UTAH:

Bald eagles are seen at Ogden Bay every winter. They usually begin to arrive in January and peak in March.

Ogden Bay freezes over during January and February except for the main running river channels. The ice thaws toward the end of March, and the eagles begin to leave when the ice completely melts.

Noland F. Nelson, Superintendent, Ogden Bay WMA, Utah

They show up with the freezing of the units, near the end of November. They usually peak in numbers in mid to late January. The eagles generally leave Farmington Bay WMA by early March.

Timothy H. Provan, Superintendent, Farmington Bay WMA, Utah

The fall migration of bald eagles through the Bear River Migratory Bird Refuge usually begins in late November or early December. The spring migration begins in late February and peaks in March.

Ned I. Peabody, Manager, Bear River Migratory Bird Refuge, U.S.D.I.

During 1974 two adult bald eagles arrived at Desert Lake WMA in early November. The next year, 1975, seven bald eagles (two adults and five juveniles) arrived in mid-November.

Bald eagles leave the Desert Lake area each year in early January when all of the waterfowl are gone due to severe weather conditions. However, in early March bald eagles return to Desert Lake along with northward bound waterfowl. Each year more adults were observed in the spring than during the fall.

Nine bald eagles were seen at Gordon Creek Wildlife Management Area periodically between November and December, 1975. No roost has yet been identified for these birds. The bald eagles at Gordon Creek are not the same bald eagles using Desert Lake, since I have seen both groups on the same day.

Larry B. Dalton, Wildlife Biologist, State Division of Wildlife Resources

The first adult bald eagles arrive at the Tintic Mountain roost, located between Rush and Cedar Valleys, between November 20th and December 1st, followed in a few days by the first immatures. Departure in the spring follows the same pattern, with adults rather abruptly departing between March 25th and 28th. A few immatures may still be around on April 12th.

Clyde C. Edwards, PhD Thesis 1969, Brigham Young University

IDAHO:

Bald eagles can be seen occasionally along southwest Idaho rivers and streams during any month of the year. Their fall buildup begins about the first of October and lasts through March.

James F. Keating, Regional Supervisor, Department of Fish & Game

The first eagles arrived at Wolf Lodge Bay (Lake Coeur d'Alene) on November 10, 1975. A gradual buildup in numbers through December resulted in a population high of 36 individuals on January 7, 1976. Compared to the total of 58 birds on January 10th of last year, a year of good salmon abundance, it is evident the food supply is an important limiting factor on how large the winter eagle population will be. The eagles began to depart the area in late January, and only five birds remained in the area on February 6th.

> *Joseph B. Lint, Wildlife Mgmt. Biologist, Bureau of Land Management*

The eagles tend to arrive during the main waterfowl movement into the refuge in the fall and return north generally after the spring migration has passed through the refuge.

> *John D. Hill, Manager, Minidoka NWR*

Late in April and early May a few pair of bald eagles will show around Grays Lake as the first migrant ducks appear at breakup. Eagles also occur in these same places in the fall. The first bald eagles usually show in October, but the greatest number is in November. At this time many of our small potholes are frozen or beginning to freeze, and the waterfowl are concentrated in the smaller areas.

> *Russell Hoffman, Manager, Grays Lake and Bear Lake NWR*

These birds usually arrive in late December and early January. They depart in late March and late April.

> *Jack L. Richardson, Manager, Camas NWR*

Bald eagles arrive in the Salmon area during late October or early November. Their departure occurs sometime in February.

> *Walter L. Bodie, Regional Game Biologist, Idaho Department of Fish & Game*

Bald eagle use of the Kootenai NWR and vicinity is light and most observations are during the October to mid-December and late February to early May periods.

> *Delano A. Pierce, Manager, Kootenai NWR*

COLORADO:

Our peak movement is November for arrival and March or early April for departure.

> *Richard Stransky, Durango Audubon Society*

Bald eagles have been observed at Blue Mesa Lake from November 14 through April 20 but are primarily seen December through March.

> *James W. Packard, Superintendent, Curecanti National Recreation Area, National Park Service*

OREGON:

The first bald eagles are usually observed about the first week in

November each year. Usually most of the birds leave the area about the first week in March.

A. Boyd Claggett, Manager, Summer Lake WMA, Oregon

They generally arrive about late October, and there is usually an immature or two that will spend the winter here.

John T. Annear, Manager, William L. Finley NWR

The bald eagles usually arrive about the first part of November. The population builds up slowly during November and reaches the peak during December and January. Some of the birds appear to leave in February and most are gone by the first of March.

John E. Kurtz, Manager, Umatilla NWR

Their presence is related to the waterfowl migration. Bald eagles appear around October 15-20, slightly past the peak of waterfowl migrations. For the basin eagle numbers may reach 30 before freeze-up in December. When the waterfowl leave, most of the bald eagles go with them. Perhaps ±15 stay during the winter. When the pintails and whistling swans move back through the area in February and March, the bald eagles return with them. A conservative peak number of bald eagles for the basin is 70. They quickly drop in number until the last depart in early April.

Larry Napier, Wildlife Biologist, Malheur NWR

OREGON/CALIFORNIA:

We note population influxes generally in late November.

Robert C. Fields, Manager, Klamath Basin NWR

CALIFORNIA:

It is my understanding that eagles arrive at Big Bear Lake in November and may be around until March or thereabouts. So far as I know there are no longer any resident bald eagles in Southern California, thus the Big Bear birds are doubless from the north.

Leo R. Best, Mt. San Antonio College, Walnut, California

The earliest arrival is in October. Most are seen in November and December. Occasionally, a bird winters in the area into January but none are seen after that. Almost without exception these are immature birds.

Don V. Tiller, Assistant Manager, Salton Sea NWR

KENTUCKY:

We can expect our first geese almost on the dot of September 20, about 50 birds. The census will build up to around 5,000 by November 1, and about that time we expect the eagles. They roost in the large, old, dead cypress trees in our overflow lakes in the resting area used by the waterfowl. I have seen as many as six in one tree at a time.

James O. Moynahan, Manager, Ballard WMA, Kentucky

TENNESSEE:

Land-Between-the-Lakes typically has three to five wintering golden eagles in addition to the bald eagles. Early migrants generally begin arriving in mid-September with peak concentrations occurring in late January and early February. Most wintering eagles depart in March but a few have remained as late as early April.

Thomas H. Ripley, Director, Division of Wildlife Development, TVA

We usually get our first birds in mid to late October. Subsequently, they build onward to a peak sometime during January or February. They begin leaving during March and about all are gone by April 1.

Wendell E. Crews, Manager, Reelfoot Lake NWR

ARKANSAS:

Average dates for first fall sighting through last spring sighting would be November 15 through March 15.

Paul D. Daly, Manager, Holla Bend NWR

TEXAS:

The eagles arrive in late November through early December and leave about early February. There are no March records. The individuals winter only and are never seen during fall, spring, or summer. Thus, they are almost surely members of the northern race.

Dan H. Hardy, Houston, Texas, (Publication: The Spoonbill)

The migrant bald eagles usually arrive at Buffalo Lake Refuge about the second week of December and peak in January. The bald eagles follow the waterfowl migration peaks and usually depart the second week of March, but no later than the second week of April.

Larry Wynn, Buffalo Lake NWR, Umbarger, Texas

NEW MEXICO:

The eagles usually arrive with the wintering snowgeese in November and leave with them in February.

Larry R. Ditto, Assistant Manager, Bosque del Apache NWR

WASHINGTON:

Most of the bald eagles that occur from about November through March are immature; it is probable that the adult balds sighted are year-round breeding residents.

Highest eagle counts are registered in late January to early and mid-February. Migration starts about March 1 and continues at low levels through April, and even into May.

Most of the movement is by immature bald eagles. Although certain adults may leave the island from time to time, they return to their nest territory after a short absence of perhaps two to three weeks. Thus, the adults are not generally considered migratory.

Spring migration produces a significant decrease in immature eagle population levels—by about 75 percent. However, adult levels remain more or less constant. The immatures, which summer here, *may* be island-bred; but this is only an assumption based on their observed rapid development of efficient techniques for rabbit predation/scavenging. The bald eagle numbers remain relatively constant through the summer months at about 20 to 30 bald eagles island-wide. The situation is roughly the same for the remainder of the San Juan Archipelago, which in total, has about the same population as San Juan Island. Fall movement begins about mid to late August. It is drawn out through October and, in fact, into January.

William Stevens, National Park Service, San Juan Island

Bald eagles begin to arrive along the Skagit River in mid-October and have largely left the area by late March. There is an upsurge in numbers of adults in early December, balanced in the following weeks by increasing numbers of sub adults. "The departure of the Skagit eagles seemed to be closely related to the depletion of the food supply, and there seemed to be no difference between adults and sub adults in this response."

Christopher Servheen, MS Thesis, University of Washington (1975)

The movements of bald eagles along the west coast are virtually unknown, however, some sightings of marked birds have been recorded. In my opinion, both local movements and long-range southerly movements are occurring. Also, the wintering population still remains higher than the known breeding population.

Mark Stalmaster, Graduate Student, Huxley College of Environmental Studies

Just a few bald eagles migrate through this vicinity between November 20 and March 25. Records show the first bald eagles arrive in November. Evidently, they are migrating through the area. This is probably due to open water. During the fall-winter waterfowl season, their presence could be influenced by crippled waterfowl and available food fish. These birds do not stay long on the refuge.

James R. Good, Assistant Refuge Manager, Columbia NWR

BRITISH COLUMBIA, CANADA

There is no indication that bald eagles are moving down-coast in winter, except perhaps for large concentrations attracted by salmon runs on a seasonal basis.

Similarly, there is no indication that bald eagles desert interior areas in winter. While detailed counts have not been conducted, subjective impressions indicate that densities are as great in winter as summer along interior river valleys. Again, however, the birds tend to concentrate seasonally near food sources such as salmon runs.

It is possible that these seasonal concentrations of birds on both the coast and in the interior are derived from a wide area. However, it seems more probable that these concentrations represent merely local shifts in location.

I. D. Smith, Inventory Coordinator, Fish & Wildlife Branch, Department of Recreation and Conservation

5
Exploratory Migratory Movements

The central and western United States fills up each fall with bald eagles, then empties again in March and April leaving only a "rim" of resident nesting birds in the northern-border and Pacific coast states. In order to determine where, and how far, eagles travel on these annual migrations, a very select (authorized) group of raptor biologists climb to the lofty nests and affix numbered leg bands to the fledgling eagles. This is an arduous task by all standards, for the nests are widely separated, often in remote areas, and typically difficult of access.

"Chance" largely dictates whether the bird and its identifying band will come into the hands of another person who will establish a second reference point in the eagle's travels. In the past most recovery records are from eagles found dead or wounded. With severe penalties placed on shooting eagles, and every effort made to reduce accidental death, other means must be found to read these registered numbers. Thus far live trap, examine, and release unharmed, has met with little success on this large raptor.

Bird banding in North America is officially administered by the U.S. Fish and Wildlife Service and the Canadian Wildlife Service. All banders must be covered by a federal permit. The bands direct the finder to send his information to the Fish and Wildlife Service, Washington, D.C., and the incoming data winds up at the Bird Banding Laboratory, Patuxent Wildlife Research Center, Laurel, Maryland. There the record is entered on computer tapes and a North American registry maintained. First publication rights to this data are reserved for the person who initially marked the bird. This must be kept in mind when seeking information from this central registry.

75

Since 1955, approximately 2,000 bald eagles have been banded. With the increased interest in the welfare of this species, some 300 to 400 new band-carrying eagles will probably be added each year. As of August, 1975, only 232 returns had been filed with the Bird Banding Laboratory, but only about half of this number are bald eagles banded on their northern nesting grounds. So progress is painfully slow.

A second approach to the tracking of individual eagles is by affixing a colored "disc" to the leading edge of the wing, which in no way impairs the bird's flight but permits identification of a free-roaming bird from a distance. The combination of several colored discs identify an area from which birds originated. A yet further improvement is to include a large letter or numeral against the colored disc, thereby making it possible to identify an individual bird and relate it to an official numbered leg band that the bird also wears.

At increasing number of sites where bald eagles congregate each winter to take advantage of a local food source, resident area managers are establishing blinds for study and photography of the assembled birds. In other locations, the socially minded bald eagles have become so conditioned to automobiles that close approach (100 to 150 feet) to perching or feeding eagles is possible. Thus, the opportunity to record color-coded eagles and thus establish multiple reference points in their travels is improving.

The last, and most sophisticated technique, is to attach a tiny radio transmitter to the bird, and then by means of a directional receiver and antenna, mounted on automobile and aircraft, actually follow the wanderings of the bird for periods of one to two months. This technology has been extensively used by researchers on the Chippewa National Forest Eagle Nesting Area.

During the period 1964-74, the following raptor biologists banded 1,375 bald eagles in the northern tier of states and in Canada. By 1975 there had been 65 second point recoveries. Using this data, and 45 recoveries resulting from the work of other banders, this group is preparing a manuscript for publication which will bring our present information up to date and in useful form.

Dr. Jonathan M. Gerrard	James B. Holt
Sergej Postupalsky	Allen K. Jacobsen
David L. Evans	Charles R. Sindelar, Jr.
James W. Grier	Douglas W. A. Whitfield

A nestling bald eagle banded by Dr. Thomas Dunstan in June, 1968, in Itasca County, Minnesota, was recovered four months later dead, some 16 miles south of Llano, Texas. Another bald eagle from the very same home range in Itasca County, Minnesota, was banded in June, 1971. This second bird also made its way to Texas being caught in a coyote trap near Matador, Texas, in January, 1973. This is a distance of over 1,200 miles from where these two bald eagles were hatched.

Abstracted from:
"First Recovery of a Bald Eagle Banded in Minnesota"
Thomas C. Dunstan, Loon Vol. 41:92 (1969) and Vol. 45/132 (1973)

Bresnard lake is situated in northcentral Saskatchewan about 35 miles northwest of La Ronge. It is about 62 square miles in area with an irregular shoreline some 250 miles long. The lake has many islands. In 1973 there were 26 to 27 bald eagle breeding areas on Bresnard Lake. Eighteen young from thirteen nests were individually marked with different combinations of red, yellow, and green vinyl wing markers. This enabled Dr. Gerrard and his associates to follow the young eagles during the post-fledgling period of six to seven weeks. Thereafter these immature eagles headed south. Sightings of the color marked eagles were subsequently made in North Dakota (October), South Dakota (October and November), Missouri (November), and off to the West in Wyoming (December).

Abstracted from:
"Post Fledgling Movements of Juvenile Bald Eagles"
Peter Gerrard, Jonathan M. Gerrard, Douglas W. A. Whitefield, and William J. Maher.
The Blue Jay 32 (4): 218-225, December of 1974

The work of James F. Harper and Dr. Thomas C. Dunstan provides an excellent introduction into the use of radio-telemetry to follow bald eagles. Miniature radio-transmitters, weighing from 24 to 40 grams, with a battery life of approximately eight months, were attached via back-pack harness to six to eight week old eagles during the month of June. The radio package did not encumber the bird's movements and was designed to eventually fall off. Two eagles were tagged in 1971, three in 1972, and fifteen in 1974. Pulsing signals from the transmitters were received on an AVM model LA-12 tracking receiver using a directional yagi antenna. Reception range was on a line-of-sight, anywhere from ½ to 20 miles. Cross-country tracking was done by car and a Cessna 150.

In addition to the study of behavioral patterns for young bald eagles in the period immediately after leaving the nest, these investigators followed the initial legs of the migratory flight. One bird that took off in a southwesterly direction was tracked for 410 miles. The longest flight in one day was 170 miles in nine hours.

Abstracted from:
"Dispersal and Migration of Fledgling Bald Eagles"
James F. Harper and Thomas C. Dunstan, Western Illinois University, Macomb, Illinois
Presented February 1, 1976, at Bald Eagle Days, Madison, Wisconsin

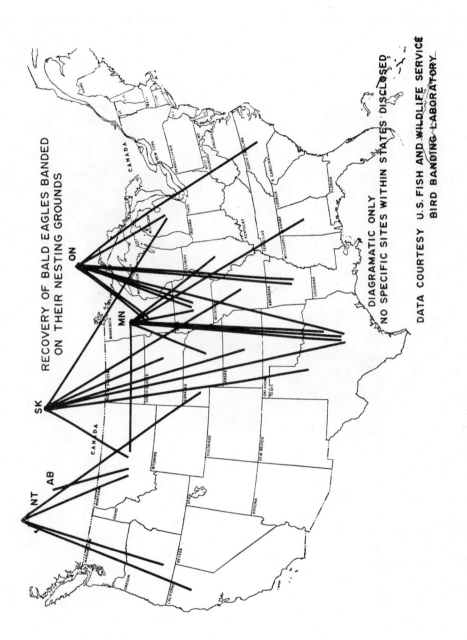

6
Dams, Hydroelectric Plants, and Warm Water Effluents

In this century, water management programs have markedly changed the face of this nation. On the Great Plains and in the arid Intermountain and Southwestern United States, there are permanent sources of water where in previous time it was only seasonably available. Oklahoma and Kansas are now studded with large lakes and impoundments, stocked for fishing and attracting wintering waterfowl. Without intent, man has created a greatly expanded wintering habitat for bald eagles.

In the northern tier of States, many a major waterway is characterized by a series of dams and locks having multipurpose use (navigation, flood control, power generation, water storage, recreation, etc.). In areas where the rivers and lakes regularly freeze over, these locks and dams provide open water in the severest weather—having the advantage of retaining an overwintering population of waterfowl and their bald eagle attendants.

Water passing through the turbines of hydroelectric plants, stuns or kills any fish caught up in the intake. These are served up to waiting bald eagles who gather along the tailrace of the dam.

Even the much maligned heated effluents from industrial and power plants sited on these impoundments increase the carrying capacity of the area for bald eagles. Not only do these heated effluents keep water areas from freezing over but it attracts the abundant gizzard shad, and because rapid temperature changes can occur when shut down repairs are necessary, delivers up a fish kill for the eagles.

81

MISSISSIPPI RIVER IMPOUNDMENTS:

The major birding features of the Upper Mississippi River are the Locks and Dams and Power Plants which create open water below and above. The locks and dams were built in the 1930's and were completed in 1939. The power plants have gradually been added as the need for more electrical power has increased. These have caused some major changes in bird populations, notably the winter concentrations of bald eagles. The number of eagles has increased until now the Mississippi River has a greater winter population of bald eagles than any other area in the nation except Alaska.

From: Wintering Birding Along the Mississippi River
By: Elton Fawks and Terrence N. Ingram

ILLINOIS:

Distribution of eagles on the district appears to be directly correlated with the presence of a combination of open water and undisturbed roosting area. Open water occurs primarily below the locks and dams and below the Cordova Nuclear plant. These areas are where the eagles concentrate during the winter. During cold spells the open water areas become rather small forcing the birds to leave the district. This usually occurs in most years during late January resulting in a significant reduction in the eagle population present.

Thomas D. Atkins, District Manager, Upper Mississippi River NWR, Savanna District

On the Mississippi River, below Lock and Dam 19 (and a power plant), researchers from Western Illinois University determined that between Mink and Mud Islands there was a current where dead fish floated, such as gizzard shad, freshwater brown, and goldeneye, which made easy prey for bald eagles from the Cedar Glen Eagle Roost. It would appear that 70 to 80 percent of the prey coming through were decapitated small gizzard shad. In some cases, in a 300 foot wide stretch of the main current, some 60 to 70 dead gizzard shad floated by in a ten-minute period. At other times less than ten fish.

Dr. Tom Dunstan, Proceedings of the Bald Eagle Days 1975
(Report Condensed By Editor)

MISSOURI:

Most of the area wintering bald eagles in January will be found just below the dam feeding on fish.

Glen R. Miller, Manager, Cannon & Delair Divisions, Mark Twain NWR

IOWA:

Gizzard shad are highly vulnerable to winter stress conditions and are prime targets for eagle in this area.

When the weather becomes extremely cold, about the only open water on the Mississippi is below the navigation dams and near the warm water effluents of power plants and the like. Fossil fuel plants are good feeding areas as the warm water discharges often flow through a short canal to the river. These never freeze and attract great numbers of shad in stressed condition. Other species, such as drum and mooneye, are present but in lesser numbers.

The open areas below navigation dams, on the other hand, being kept open by turbulence are not so conducive to accumulation of stressed fish. Rather, fish drifting down stream and through the dam are swept near the surface and can be plucked out by an eagle. Likewise, areas of lesser turbulence, such as boils around wing dams, etc., may open temporarily during brief periods of mild weather and are fished in a similar manner.

As the river begins to thaw, there are open areas of quite water where shad can be found in abundance.

It must also be pointed out that commercial fishermen sometimes leave quantities of fish on the ice near seine hauls for eagles to feed on.
Don R. Helms, Fishery Biologist, Iowa Fisheries Research Station

SOUTH DAKOTA:

"Before 1953 and the building of the first multipurpose dam along the Missouri River, the bald eagle was only an occasional visitor to South Dakota. Since that time the wintering population, which is recorded annually along and adjacent to the Missouri between Elk Point and Pierre, has increased to approximately 300 birds."
Dr. Thomas C. Dunstan 1970
The Wintering Bald Eagle of South Dakota.
South Dakota Conservation Digest 37 (6): 12-15

"As recently as 25 years ago, there were almost no eagles in South Dakota, but over the years the Missouri River has become a major wintering roost. The area below Fort Randall Dam seems to have all of the necessary elements for eagle survival.

The dam probably supplies the most important feature of the roost— easy access to a constant supply of food. In the tailwaters the river stays open in the coldest weather, and there is an abundant supply of fish."
K. R. Moum, 1975
The Karl E. Mundt National Wildlife Refuge
South Dakota Conservation Digest 42 (2): 9-10

MISSOURI RIVER IMPOUNDMENTS:

Several of the attractants for bald eagles at these areas are:
1. Areas of open water all winter below the powerhouses.
2. Good resting and roosting areas near the open water sites.
3. Large duck populations that migrate through these areas, and some ducks that remain in the area over most of the winter.

4. Dead fish from the turbines that get washed up to the edge of the ice or float in eddies near the surface of the open water area.
Russel L. Bywater, Omaha District Corps of Engineers, U.S. Army

KANSAS:

Within four miles of the area is a large reservoir (3,000 acres) built by the Kansas City Power and Light Company. This reservoir is used for cooling water for a coal plant. An additional power plant will soon be in operation. There is a possibility that these power plants will keep the reservoir from freezing. A large die off of shad on this reservoir in 1975-76 created a large source of available food, and numerous eagles were attracted to the area.
Lloyd B. Fox, District Game Biologist, Marais des Cygnes WMA

OKLAHOMA:

Most bald eagles on Fort Gibson Reservoir were present directly below the dam. Eagles frequently perched in large sycamore trees adjacent to state Highway 80 and commonly soared over or sat in trees along the wooded bluffs on the west side of Grand River below the dam.

On the Keystone Reservoir eagles concentrated from the dam to approximately 1 kilometer downstream and in flooded timber on the Arkansas River just north of Cleveland. Eagles infrequently perched in trees just downstream from the dam.

The area just below the dam on Grand Lake is used by eagles. Eagles perched in large sycamore *(Platanus occidentalis)* trees just below the western spillway. Eagles frequently sat in large white oaks on steep bluffs, 0.05 kilometer south of the eastern spillway.
James William Lish, MS Thesis, Oklahoma State University (1975)

LOUISIANA:

The largest concentration of bald eagles in Louisiana is to be found below the spillway at Toledo Bend Lake, a sprawling 200,000 acre impoundment located on the Texas-Louisiana border. This lake was built in the mid-1960's and has a high fish population. It is also used for hydroelectricity.
S. Ray Aycock, Jr., Wildlife Biologist, U.S. Fish & Wildlife Service

WISCONSIN:

Peak numbers apparently fluctuate quite widely. Whether this is a real fluctuation or simply a faulty census technique (timing and coverage) might be questioned. I suspect that there is a real fluctuation which may be caused by ice conditions on the La Crosse District. We have no power plants on the district, whereas, Pool 9 (just below) and

Pool 5 (1 pool above) both contain power plants at their upper ends and thus more open water throughout the winter. Particularly in spring this district may be slower to "open up" than up-river areas and conversely may freeze shut in late fall before either Pool 5 or Pool 9. Thus, eagles may "over-fly" the La Crosse District in some years.

Kenneth O. Butts, Manager, La Crosse District

Necedah is 5 air miles from a hydroelectric installation on the Wisconsin River known as Petenwell dam. The tailwater of this dam is a wintering place for eagles. A short ways down stream from Petenwell is a second major dam, the Castle Rock dam. This area also provides wintering habitat for eagles. These two areas have been censused for years during the mid-winter eagle survey and normally have a combined wintering population of 15 to 25 birds. Most of these birds are adults as opposed to the refuge's fall immature population.

Dennis W. Strom, Manager, Necedah NWR

MONTANA:

Generally the Yellowstone is covered with ice during the winter, but in Billings we have a steam-generated electric plant that discharges into the Yellowstone. This raises the temperature of the water to a degree that the river is open directly below Billings and periodically for about 10 miles to Huntley, Montana. The fish in the river and the quantities of ducks on the open water make the area an ideal wintering spot for the bald eagles.

Don MacDonald, Billings, Montana, Audubon Society

IDAHO:

We saw quite a number of adult and immature bald eagles this past winter in the Orofino to Lewiston area with most of them concentrated near the dam (Dworshak Dam).

Dworshak Dam has an annual drawdown during the fall and winter months at which time fish come through the dam, over the spillway, and through the turbines. These fish, if not killed outright, are stunned and easy prey for eagles and osprey. During the fall months, some kokanee enter the hatchery through the trap at the dam, so there is fish available most of the year in the North Fork of the Clearwater below Dworshak Dam.

Wesley Cannon, Regional Fishery Manager, Idaho Fish & Game Department

7

Food and the Fall Migration

Bald Eagles *prefer* fish as food, and when fish are readily obtained, other food sources are ignored. But during the winter months ice closes much of the fishing grounds except along the coasts. In the interior, the open water sites become congested with migrant waterfowl that are subject all along the migratory routes to regulated sport hunting. Some wounded and crippled birds avoid being taken by the gunner. So without losing touch with the aquatic environment, that from time to time will have fish for the taking, the bald eagle takes advantage of an abundant, seasonally concentrated, secondary source of food—waterfowl.

Crippled waterfowl are such an important supplement to the fall and winter food of the bald eagle that most observers report that eagle numbers flucutate with the numbers of waterfowl present. Thus the sportsman's financed programs to build and maintain a huntable population of waterfowl has long been laying the foundation that makes the United States a livable wintering ground for the bald eagle. Even the inept gunner who only succeeds in delayed-crippling of his quarry plays into the "talons" of bald eagles by making capture almost a certainty.

In addition to utilizing any and all species of waterfowl found dead or trapped in the ice, bald eagles will harass a flock into flight, isolate a crippled or slow-reacting individual, which is subsequently killed and eaten.

Certain species of waterfowl are more vulnerable to predation by bald eagles than others. Geese are the preferred prey by all accounts, even though once in the air a healthy goose can often elude his eagle pursuer. In most instances the bald eagle does not seem interested in the long chase. Birds that dive below the water's surface to escape capture are difficult prey for the bald eagle. Yet repeated harassment with several eagles taking part may drive such prey to shallow water or simply tire it out.

The bald eagle, except when food is scarce, rarely exerts itself by taking other than dead or disadvantaged prey. It utilizes effectively what would otherwise be a wasted resource. However, under complete protection, eagle populations can over-reach this expendable food source and is then capable of local predation on species we would rather not lose—like the whistling swans at Desert Lake Wildlife Management Area in Utah.

As the winter progresses, ducks and geese that utilize an open-water site for resting, but feed during the day in fields on waste grain, may be forced to move on by snow cover. Any eagle electing to stay behind must now turn to another alternate source of food—carrion. Since road kills, trapper and hunter discards, and weather casualties of livestock and big game animals are a dispersed source of food, the eagles range widely over the uplands. In some sections of the Great Plains and Intermountain Regions, this food source assumes major survival value—an important seasonal extension of the migrant bald eagle's wintering territory.

MINNESOTA:

The food base on Agassiz Refuge appears to be the sick and injured waterfowl present during the fall hunting season. The fishery base on the refuge is quite limited and does not appear to supply a significant quantity of food to eagles.

Joseph Kotok, Manager, Agassiz NWR

WISCONSIN:

The main food bald eagles have been observed eating on the refuge are crippled Canadian geese. The eagles utilize this otherwise wasted resource quite effectively.

Dennis W. Strom, Manager, Necedah NWR

The main food base for the eagles is the large concentration of Canadian geese that use the refuge. Hunting in the Horicon Zone provides a good food base for bald and golden eagles. The marsh usually is frozen up by mid-November.

Thomas S. Sanford, Manager, Horicon NWR

Crippled ducks in the fall, and muskrats, are taken by bald eagles, but fish is the main diet.

In the fall of 1974, there was an unusual case of three bald eagles (two adults and one immature) raiding, for at least a month, a domestic goose farm about 25 miles west of Alma, Wisconsin.

Hilma L. Volk, Assistant Manager, Winona District, Upper Mississippi River NWR

The primary food source for eagles on the La Crosse District appears to be fish. Most fish are taken from the water by the eagles and some are taken from the ice (commercial fishing operations). Another food source, particularly during the fall migration, is waterfowl. Eagles frequently harass flocks of ducks and apparently pick off many dead or crippled birds.

Kenneth O. Butts, Manager, La Crosse District, Upper Mississippi River NWR

IOWA:

In October the food base is primarily crippled waterfowl, and in April mostly rough fish and some waterfowl.

Jack C. Womble, Manager, Union Slough NWR

ILLINOIS:

Fall eagle use correlates roughly with waterfowl use, and most foods are available as a result of hunter-related crippled and dead birds.

Tom J. Early, District Manager, Mark Twain NWR, Louisa & Keithsburg District

The main food the bald eagles eat are dead or sick waterfowl; however, fish also comprise some of their diet. Usually there is open water in the lower pool of the Lake Chautauqua where spring water flows into the refuge. Also, Quiver Creek, which runs adjacent to the refuge, is spring fed and provides open water during colder weather. Together they provide feeding sites when most pool areas, and sometimes the Illinois River, are frozen over.

Howard A. Lipke, Manager, Chautauqua District, Mark Twain NWR

Of course, the eagles occur in and around areas where food is most readily available: locks and dams on the rivers where they feed primarily on fish and near the conservation areas where crippled ducks and geese are utilized.

James M. Lockart, Supervisor, Division of Wildlife Resources, Illinois Department of Conservation

They fed on fish (shad) they caught, on carp left on the ice after seine hauls for buffalo, and on a garbage dump. There was open water at the lock and dam and from springs along the sand banks at the Depot.

Herbert G. Troester, Savanna Dist., Upper Miss. River NWR

KENTUCKY:

I have observed them feeding on geese and ducks which have been crippled by hunters. In one instance I saw an eagle kill a duck in the air, but I have not seen one kill a healthy goose. I have observed two or three sitting in a tree watching a crippled goose on the ice. Later when I would go back, the kill would have been made; and they would be feeding. I have not observed them feed on anything but geese and ducks.

James O. Moynahan, Manager, Ballard WMA, Kentucky

TENNESSEE:

Although reservoir fishes are doubtless staple food items, peak concentrations of wintering eagles coincide with concentrations of wintering waterfowl. Guntersville Lake and the Land-Between-The-Lakes area have large populations of wintering waterfowl with concentrations of eagles occurring in reservoir regions used by waterfowl. Wheeler Reservoir is an exception in that it winters large waterfowl populations but receives limited use by eagles probably as a consequence of the large amount of industrial and residential development.

Thomas H. Ripley, Director, Division of Wildlife Development TVA

MISSOURI:

Normally, the eagles feed on goose carcasses. There have been a few unconfirmed reports of eagles attacking live geese, but these would be rare occasions indeed. If we suffer a winter-kill of fish, the eagles turn their attentions to the dead fish, but I am confident that it is the large numbers of geese (150,000 to 175,000) that draws them here and is their food base.

Alfred O. Manke, Manager, Swan Lake NWR

The eagles follow the waterfowl migration and feed mainly on weak and crippled snow geese in addition to a few mallards and Canadian geese. During a normal winter the refuge pools are frozen from mid-December to mid-February, and the eagles disperse after their food supply dwindles, which usually occurs in January. When we experience a mild winter, however, the eagles remain because there are always some geese and ducks that come back here when our pools partially reopen a few times during the winter.

Gerald M. Nugent, Manager, Squaw Creek NWR

The food base most likely to attract and hold these migrants is other birds, especially waterfowl, since at this time up to 27,000 Canadian geese and over 200,000 ducks may feed in the area. Waterfowl hunting occurs on the adjacent Duck Creek State Game Management Area and in the surrounding area so there is some crippling loss during and after the waterfowl season whereby these birds are utilized as prey.

Gerald L. Clawson, Manager, Mingo NWR

Openings appeared on the water bodies February 10, 1976. Waterfowl began returning February 11; the first eagles appeared February 12. No eagle feeding was observed this spring, however, they were constantly seen in conjunction with large numbers of ducks. Also, one adult eagle was observed in a harvested soybean field, 100 feet from a marsh hawk eating a dead mallard. It is suspected that the duck flew into a nearby electrical line either injuring or killing itself. Waterfowl populations on Cannon Refuge from February 17 to March 5 have been anywhere from 60,000 to 100,000.

Glen R. Miller, Manager, Cannon and Delair Divisions, Mark Twain NWR

The main food source is Canadian goose, however, this may be supplemented by a winter-kill of rough fish. Eagles tend to follow the movements of Canadian goose concentrations.

Robert Dobbins, Manager, Fountain Grove WMA, Missouri

KANSAS:

The primary food that the eagles on Glen Elder/Waconda Lake have been observed to feed on is dead, sick, and crippled ducks, primarily mallards as they make up the largest component of our wintering population. Fish, primarily winter-killed gizzard shad, are also available; and the eagles have been observed feeding on them also. The use of fish by eagles is not as common but does occur. From the month of December to February when most eagle use occurs, mallards are abundant (100,000 or more during most of that period). As duck numbers decline in late February and March, many of the eagles also leave. On occasion they will pick up any slow reacting waterfowl, likely cripples. For the most part the waterfowl usage is on mallard ducks, and it is a very slight usage at that.

Ken Garrigues, Manager, Cheney WMA, Kansas

Wounded and sick waterfowl are the main food base which holds these birds on the refuge area. Normally, the lake freezes over about the first of the year and remains ice covered, except for three to four waterholes kept open by the waterfowl until near the end of February. The waterholes vary in size during this period from only a few acres to perhaps close to 100 acres depending upon the weather. It is real common to see the eagles on the ice around these waterholes.

Keith S. Hansen, Manager, Kirwin NWR

Bald eagles begin to show up at Cheyenne Bottoms in late December as soon as the area freezes over completely. It seems that the freeze up makes any crippled ducks and geese more available prey. During December and January I have seen bald eagles feed primarily on ducks and geese. An occasional pheasant or carp is also utilized.

Bob Bartels, District Game Biologist, Cheyenne Bottoms WMA

The eagles are attracted to the area by waterfowl concentrations. The foods that I have observed the eagles feeding upon include mallard, common merganser, coot, snow geese, muskrat, and numerous species of fish, the most important being the gizzard shad. A comprehensive food study of the wintering bald eagles at the Marais des Cygnes WMA has not been undertaken.

Lloyd B. Fox, District Game Biologist, Marais des Cygnes WMA

The eagles feed on dead shad or other fish floating in water and crippled or injured ducks they catch. The area around Lake McKinney also has a good rabbit population. In cold weather it was not uncommon to see two or three eagles fighting over a duck on ice with crows and magpies waiting to clean up scraps.

Bruce C. Peters, District Game Protector, Lakin, Kansas

Eagle food at Lake McKinney is mainly fish (carp, some channel cats) and waterfowl. I have personally observed bald eagles eating carp and dead ducks frozen in the ice at Lake McKinney.

Robert J. Price, District Game Biologist, Lake McKinney WMA

OKLAHOMA:

We believe these eagles feed primarily on fish with waterfowl forming a substantial part of the diet. Bald eagles have been observed pursuing snow geese and feeding on snow goose remains. When there are particularly high concentrations of ducks, we notice more eagles tend to gather in close proximity to the duck resting areas. However, we have not actually seen eagles feeding on or chasing ducks.

Robert H. Stratton, Jr., Manager, Sequoyah NWR

The population is pretty much spread out over the refuge, however, occasionally several eagles may be seen near the same goose carcass.

Jerry C. Sturdy, Assistant Manager, Tishomingo NWR

The wintering bald eagles at the Wichita spend considerable time around the larger lakes at the refuge. These waters contain most of the warm water species of fish found at this latitude. Several hundred ducks, mostly gadwall, also use these waters during the winter. However, I have not observed our bald eagles feeding on the fish or ducks.

Gene Bartnicki, Wildlife Biologist, Wichita Mountains NWR

Another important food source is wintering waterfowl. This is a major goose hunting area, and eagles are often seen hanging near the edge of loafing goose flocks to pick out wounded and weakened birds or feeding on such birds.

Ronald S. Sullivan, Manager, Salt Plains NWR

LOUISIANA:

The flooded bean fields along the Ouachita River, Spring Bayou, and Catahoula Lake attract bald eagles because of both high fish populations and large numbers of wintering waterfowl. Similar reasons exist for the other impoundments that are utilized.

S. Ray Aycock, Jr., Wildlife Biologist, U.S. Fish & Wildlife Service

TEXAS:

Frequently eagles are observed grouped on the ground in a rice stubblefield around a dead goose. There may be one to ten in one spot near a duck or goose flock, or even within a goose flock. I have never seen an eagle kill a goose and can only speculate that they feed on already dead birds.

Dan H. Hardy, Houston, Texas, (Publication: The Spoonbill)

The birds are known to feed on live fish, dead deer meat, other carrion, and wounded ducks not retrieved by hunters. Just recently, an observer reported that bald eagles were feasting on paper shell clams which are exposed by the receding lake waters due to the drought this last winter and spring.

Larry K. Nielson, Acting Superintendent, Lake Meredith National Recreational Area

NORTH DAKOTA:

The Missouri River remains open all winter below the dam from one mile to 12 or 15 miles downstream, depending on weather conditions. I strongly suspect that the big attraction for eagles is not fish but mallards wintering in the area. Last January I saw only 150 to 200 mallards in the area but in 1975 the State Game and Fish Department reported something like 3,000 mallards below the dam.

The number of eagles seems to be related to the number of ducks wintering there, and the number of ducks is related to snow cover and availability of grain in late December and January. The winter of 1974-

75 was quite open with relatively little snow cover, and an unusually
large number of ducks wintering here; this past winter there was more
snow than normal with only a few ducks wintering in the area.

David C. McGlauchlin, Manager, Audubon NWR

In early winter the food source is probably crippled waterfowl and
in late winter turns to pheasants, grouse, or possibly deer carcasses.
Winters are frequently severe with heavy snows and strong winds. The
weather and the availability of food may be the determining factor
whether birds stay over or just pass through.

Jon M. Malcolm, Manager, J. Clark Salyer NWR

SOUTH DAKOTA:

The major food sources for the eagles in the winter concentration
areas are the fish found in the tailwaters of the reservoirs (which remain unfrozen during the winter months) and the crippled ducks and
geese resulting from the fall hunting season. Although the eagles take
advantage of these concentrated food sources, they are by no means dependent on them, as witnessed by the fact that there are some wintering eagles scattered throughout South Dakota.

Warren Jackson, Director, South Dakota Division of Game & Fish

MONTANA:

On the basis of my own observations, the wintering eagles subsist
largely on fish and can be seen feeding on fish. Since there is a fair
winter population of mallards and Canadian geese, they may also eat
some dead waterfowl. It is my impression that some birds are present
throughout every winter, the number depending on the amount of open
water near the inlet. The birds may leave for short periods of time when
open water becomes limiting but then may return from nearby areas
they have moved to (along the lower Madison, for example).

P. D. Skaar, Montana State University, Bozeman

A portion of the Ravalli Refuge is open to waterfowl hunting, and
the bald eagle takes most of the crippled ducks that the hunters do not
recover. These cripples use several ponds that do not freeze. Also, the
Bitterroot River usually does not freeze over completely. Both these
water areas have an excellent supply of fish that is readily used by
eagles.

R. C. Twist, Mgr., Ravalli NWR

UTAH:

Those birds observed have stayed right on the management area for
periods of from one to three weeks feeding on ducks, coot, carp, and
discarded muskrat carcasses. (Spring migratory period).

Dallas Taylor, Supt., Public Shooting Grounds WMA

Most of the waterfowl we observed the eagles utilizing was that of crippled waterfowl. I observed two adult balds on a coyote carcass in Jan. The refuge has a stable population of the Utah Chub (Gila atraia) within all our management units and spring heads.

Michael W. Perkins, Asst. Mgr., Fish Springs NWR

Observations of bald eagles each winter showed that they preferred to snatch coots from the water over other waterfowl that were equally numerous. It is my opinion that the preference for coots by bald eagles is precipitated by coot behavior and their unwillingness to flush at the stoop of an eagle. All of the other waterfowl would flush immediately when an eagle began hunting. Once an eagle made a kill, the wheeling waterfowl would settle back to the spot from where they flushed.

During the 1974-75 winter a population of 13 whistling swans were heavily preyed upon by the bald eagles. In late December, 1974, the number of swans dwindled by one bird each day. Finally, I found a fresh kill with a bald eagle feeding on it. The swan's entrails were still "steaming" warm, and the eagle was stripping flesh from the swan's breast.

In the six-day period from January 1 to 6, 1975, one bald eagle killed three juvenile whistling swans at the same small pot hole of open water. On January 4, 1975, I observe the one remaining bald eagle flying low over the ground and drop behind a dike where I knew two whistling swans to be resting—one swan flew away. I immediately drove to this spot and found the bald eagle sitting on top of a flopping but dead swan. It appeared that the swan flushed, but only made about 8 feet before the eagle forced it to the ground. Two days later on January 6, 1975, at the same spot, the last swan was found partially eaten; and the sign in the snow indicated it was killed early that morning by an eagle.

Larry B. Dalton, Wildlife Biologist, Desert Lake WMA

In the fall bald eagles feed on sick and wounded waterfowl, pheasant, muskrat, and dead carp.

Ned I. Peabody, Manager, Bear River Migratory Bird Refuge

The eagles can be seen scaring the waterfowl into flight then attacking those left behind due to crippling or disease. In most cases the eagles will feed on the available crippled and dead birds on the area and the carp when available. There is always open water on the area but very limited during December, January, and early February.

Timothy H. Provan, Superintendent, Farmington Bay WMA, Utah

The impoundments are frozen from December 15 to March 15; the river always remains open. Fish and waterfowl are the main foods here. The birds will range out into the river canyons both above and below Brown's Park.

F. Neil Folks, Superintendent, Brown's Park WMA, Utah

What probably attracts a few eagles in January are numbers of crippled or dead waterfowl that are left over from the hunting season and trapped or frozen in the ice.

Noland F. Nelson, Superintendent, Ogden Bay WMA, Utah

IDAHO:

Concentrations of bald eagles in southwest Idaho are not caused by fish runs but result from waterfowl concentrations at Lake Lowell and C. J. Strike Reservoir. Dead and crippled ducks are the primary attraction. Sixteen to 32 bald eagles usually winter at Deer Flat National Wildlife Refuge and only a few at C. J. Strike. These areas become extremely important during severe freezes, and the birds depend on dead and crippled waterfowl that are available on the ice. They stay as long as the food is available.

James F. Keating, Regional Supervisor, Department of Fish and Game

I personally feel that fish provide very little attraction along the Snake River in Idaho for these birds in the winter time as there is not an abundance of carcasses for them to feed on. Therefore, I do not feel that the abundance of eagles is tied to the availability of fish in this area. However, the abundance of eagles may be tied to the numbers of crippled waterfowl which increases during the fall months.

John T. Heimer, Fishery Manager, Department of Fish & Game, Region No. 5

The primary food this winter has probably been carrion and ducks.

Jack L. Richardson, Manager, Camas NWR

The main item that attracts them to the refuge is probably the numerous crippled ducks during the fall and the masses of migrating waterfowl during the spring.

Delano A. Pierce, Manager, Kootenai NWR

NEVADA:

Coots occasionally provide a food source for eagles.

R. V. Papike, Manager, Ruby Lake NWR

NEW MEXICO:

The wintering birds feed primarily on crippled waterfowl plus occasional winter fish kill remains.

Milton B. Suthers, Assistant Manager, Maxwell NWR

Probably the major food source that attracts the eagles are the ducks and geese that winter on the refuge. They pick up sick and dead birds daily and find a sufficient supply of food. They also occasionally feed on fish but not nearly as much as waterfowl.

Fred L. Bolwahnn, Manager, Las Vegas NWR

Geese are their principal prey species, but wintering ducks and coots are attractive as well.

Larry R. Ditto, Assistant Manager, Bosque del Apache NWR

BRITISH COLUMBIA, CANADA:

There appear to be at least three significant food sources for British Columbia bald eagles: First, spawning salmon; second fish and ducks along the coast; and third, carrion of all types. The outer coast represents an excellent source of the latter at all times of the year, and thus (particularly in winter) eagles tend to be regularly spaced along the coast.

I. D. Smith, Inventory Coordinator, Fish & Game Branch, Department of Recreation & Conservation

OREGON:

Main food source during that period is crippled waterfowl.
John T. Annear, Manager, William L. Finley NWR

The bald eagle population seems to have increased on Umatilla NWR over the past five years. We suspect it is because of the availability of crippled and sick ducks and geese. We currently winter nearly 200,000 ducks and 100,000 geese. There is open water on the Columbia River throughout the winter.

John E. Kurtz, Manager, Umatilla NWR

OREGON/CALIFORNIA:

The food base that attracts them is deer roadkills and crippled/diseased waterfowl.
Robert C. Fields, Manager, Klamath Basin NWR

CALIFORNIA:

When there is water or at least when there is open water in the lake in winter, waterfowl, especially coots, congregate there in fairly large numbers. Even though the whole Big Bear Lake area is very heavily used for recreation, the eagles are attracted there presumably by the food supply afforded by the waterfowl. They tend to have perching spots in the tall Jeffrey pines and mountain junipers around the lake, and can sometimes be seen on the ground at isolated points along the shore or on the ice. One was seen eating a fish on the dry lake bottom of Baldwin Lake just east of Big Bear on our last count.

In winter the eagles can obtain food, often without much effort on their part, as coots and ducks get trapped or isolated in small open spots of water as the lake freezes. There is also sporadic shooting with resultant cripples.

Leo R. Best, Mt. San Antonio College, Walnut, California

MAINE:

Observations include feeding on waterfowl (goldeneyes and mergansers) and gulls; eels may form a very important part of the diet.
Francis J. Gramlich, U.S. Fish & Wildlife Service

SOUTH CAROLINA:

The basic source is, no doubt, injured or sick waterfowl. On occasion eagles have been seen feeding on dead fish left stranded when water was released from flooded pools.
John P. Davis, Manager, Savannah & Associate Islands NWR

ALABAMA:

As for food we know they scavange dead fish along the shore lines regularly and that they take some crippled geese and ducks. Normally, we sight eagles around our largest waterfowl concentration.
Thomas Z. Atkeson, Manager, Wheeler NWR

WYOMING:

We find the eagles associated with a variety of prey species, but usually they are found near open water areas where rough fish and waterfowl might be abundant. There is no set rule however.
George F. Wrakestraw, Supervisor, Waterfowl Management, Wyoming Game & Fish Department

COLORADO:

The food source that is attracting the birds is primarily a wintering population of mallard ducks.
Charles R. Bryant, Manager, Monte Vista NWR

8

Spawning Runs of Fish

When winter comes to the northland, a favored few bald eagles head directly for a *regularly occurring* and *readily available* food source—a late fall spawning run of fish. A fairly long-lived bird with a leaning toward communal existence in the off-breeding season, there is every opportunity to learn to chart a course to exploit such fortuitous—albeit transient—sources of food. All along the coasts of Alaska and British Columbia, these spawning runs of fish are the seasonal "gathering places" for bald eagles resident in the general area.

Two traditional salmon runs in the State of Washington are of a size that attracts large numbers of bald eagles: the Nooksack River hosting about 100 eagles, and the Skagit River with 100 to 200 eagles.

Whereas anadromous fish runs in coastal streams in the United States have declined sharply in the last 100 years, a comparable source of spawned-out fish is now found far inland. A small land-locked salmon called Kokanee has been successfully established in any number of large, cold water lakes. Like their ocean-running relatives, these fish when mature move enmass up tributary streams of the lake to lay eggs and then to die. Some of these Kokanee populations date back 50 years or better, like that in Flathead Lake in Montana. The run of fish from this lake attracts the largest concentration of bald eagles on record in the lower 48 states. Other established Kokanee populations, like that in Vallecito Reservoir in southwest Colorado are of very recent origin, yet the bald eagles already home-in on them.

Wintering aggregations of migrant bald eagles locked-in to a Kokanee run are presently found in California, Oregon, Idaho, Montana, Colorado, and New Mexico. Alternate foods, such as crippled waterfowl and big game carrion, are not accepted as long as the supply of spawned-out and dying fish are available, demonstrating the unequivocal preference for fish. The supply exhausted, the bald eagles transfer to yet another location, often to be satisfied with foods lower on the preference list.

Mr. Gebhards commented in his discussion of Kokanee and bald eagles in Idaho, that the early spawning runs were probably of little importance for the northern migrant eagle because they were terminated by mid-October. However, in an area having resident bald eagles, as in northern California, these early Kokanee runs may well contribute to the area's capacity for bald eagles.

99

WASHINGTON:

Of the eight species of salmon and sea-run trout entering the Skagit to spawn, only salmon are utilized by the eagles, principally chinook, chum, and pink. Dead, spawned-out salmon, which are washed onto gravel bars or lay in shallow water near shore are fed upon. No eagle was observed to capture, or attempt to capture, a live salmon although dying salmon in shallow riffles were numerous and in clear view at certain times of the season.

Christopher Servheen, MS Thesis, University of Washington (1975)

The North Fork of the Nooksack provides excellent salmon spawning habitats for all five Pacific coast species. Small side-channels, sloughs, and large gravel bars allow spawned-out fish to wash up and provide carrion for eagles and other scavengers. Surely, this is the main stimulus for such a large concentration of birds.

In addition, I've noticed differential availability of salmon carcasses among the five different species. Those species selecting redd sites with low water velocity are least susceptible to washing away by high flood waters and thus provide a greater proportion of usable carrion.

Mark Stalmaster, Graduate Student, Huxley College of Environmental Studies

OREGON:

During the months of October through December, a concentration of adult and juvenile bald eagles build up at Sheep Bridge and the head of the Cultus River. Approximately 70 are the most that have been counted at one time. An average of 40 birds is the "normal" population during this period of time.

This eagle buildup coincides with the kokanee spawning runs out of Wickiup and Crane Prairie Reservoirs. After the fish run is over, the birds disperse and normally leave the forest. These birds probably end up in the Klamath Marsh or Summer Lake areas.

John C. Capp, Wildlife Staff Officer, Deschutes National Forest

MONTANA:

The Montana State Fish and Game Department estimates that between 75,000 and 150,000 salmon are spawning annually in McDonald Creek. They originate from a population of kokanee salmon that were introduced into Flathead Lake about 1916 (thus a man-made situation that did not formerly exist).

B. Riley McClelland, Autumn Concentrations of Bald Eagles in Glacier National Park, The Condor, 75 (1): 121-123 1973.

I believe an average of six (kokanee) salmon per eagle per day would be a fair estimate during the peak of the greatest food abundance. If this is a true figure, then during the periods of peak eagle numbers, about 1,550 salmon were eaten each day along the 7 miles of creek and river.

   David S. Shea, McDonald Creek, Glacier National Park

CALIFORNIA:

Another wintering area supporting from 10 to 30 bald eagles is located on the Papoose Arm of Clair Engle Lake, Trinity County. These birds include some residents and are feeding on spawning kokanee salmon. Arrival and dispersal information is unknown.

A wintering population, ranging from one to twelve eagles, use the Tua Lumne River near La Grange, California. Numbers appear to be correlated with the king salmon runs.

   Robert D. Mallette, Associate Wildlife Manager/Biologist, California State

Kokanee reproduce naturally in a number of lakes and reservoirs in northern California. Some of the more successful examples, the main spawning tributary, and the approximate spawning time are listed below.

   Donner Lake-Donner Creek—late October to mid-November
   Lake Tahoe-Taylor Creek—late October to mid-November
   Folsom Lake-So. Fork American River—late Oct. to mid-Nov.
   Pardee Lake-Mokelumne River—late Oct. to mid-Nov.
   Camanche Lake-Mokelumne River—late Oct. to mid-Nov.
   Bucks Lake-Bucks Creek—late Oct. to mid-Nov.
   Trinity (Clair Engle) Lake—15 to 30 tributaries whose importance varies from year to year—early run from Sept. to early Oct., and late run in December
   Whiskey Lake-Clear Creek—both early and late runs.
   G. W. McCammon, Chief of Inland Fisheries Branch, California Department of Fish and Game.

Kokanee salmon, the non-anadromous form of the sockeye salmon were first introduced into California in 1941.

In recent years, kokanee have been transplanted to Oregon, Nevada, California, Arizona, Colorado, Wyoming, and some eastern states, plus augmenting natural populations in Washington, Idaho, and Montana.

Early-spawning kokanee populations have been planted in 16 California lakes. Late spawning strains of Kokanee have been stocked in 33 California lakes, 17 of which have also received plants of early spawning fish.

   Abstracted from: Kokanee Report by Charles M. Seeley and George W. McCammon.

IDAHO:

It is assumed that the spawned-out kokanee salmon *(Oncorhynchus nerka)* were the reason for the bald eagle concentration at Wolf Lodge

Bay. Kokanee salmon were first introduced into Lake Coeur d'Alene in 1937, and since have been established into a viable breeding population. These salmon mature at about four years of age and reach a length of 12 inches. They breed during November and December of each year, then die, thus creating a readily available and easily obtainable supply of food for the bald eagles.

Joseph B. Lint, Wildlife Biologist, Bureau of Land Management

The largest concentrations of bald eagles coincide with our largest kokanee populations in the state, namely, Pend Oreille Lake and Coeur d'Alene Lake. These fish spawn in streams and lake shorelines from late November into January. Fish spawning runs in other waters are probably not a factor in the overwintering of eagles since salmon and early spawning kokanee have completed spawning by mid-October. Whitefish spawn in November and December and are widespread statewide. Since they feed actively during the winter in riffle areas, they would be available to eagles throughout the entire winter.

Stacy Gebhards, Chief, Bureau of Fisheries, Idaho Fish & Game Department

COLORADO:

Vallecito Reservoir is a large lake to the northeast of Durango. The Division of Wildlife has stocked this lake with land-locked salmon (kokanee). During the fall spawning season, I have seen as many as 25 adult bald eagles (no immatures present at this sighting) all were feeding on the dead or dying fish. Spawning takes place in October, and this usually marks the beginning of the winter eagles. After the salmon are gone, the birds seem to spread out over the area. Another major wintering ground is the Navajo Reservoir. This is a very large body of water with the dam in New Mexico with the water backing up some 18 miles into Colorado near Arboles, Colorado. The upper portion usually does not freeze making ideal wintering areas. (Also, stocked with kokanee by New Mexico Department of Game and Fish.)

Richard Stransky, Durango Audubon Society

9

Inland Fisheries
and Fish Kills

During the winter months fish kills are rather common, some regular and predictable, like below a hydroelectric plant. But sharp temperature fluctuations or an oxygen depletion under snow-covered ice can result in a massive kill—particularly of the abundant and sensitive shad. Even though such incidents occur erratically, it is astonishing how quickly word gets around to bald eagles in the general area who "drop everything" and join the crush at the unscheduled banquet.

In late winter the attention of the northward-moving bald eagles becomes seriously focused on locating lakes and ponds just at the ice-break up stage, where dead ice-entrapped fish are a reliable source of food. While waterfowl are also moving back to their nesting grounds at this same time, there is not the dependence on crippled birds as during the fall migrations.

103

KANSAS:

As to the food source which the eagles utilize while at Cheney Reservoir, personal observations are that they feed almost entirely on gizzard shad which die off in large numbers during a freeze up on the reservoir. They may be readily observed feeding along the ice edge as the lake thaws and the ice breaks up. They, of course, will pick up any other fish available as well.

After the ice pack melts, the eagles will work the shore lines for the fish until the source is exhausted or until the large numbers of public once again begin fishing or otherwise using the reservoir. Normally, the public usage occurs first, and the eagles depart from Cheney.

Ken Garrigues, Manager, Cheney WMA, Kansas

The Little Salt Marsh usually has a good population of carp which may also be a food source. The refuge suffered severe flood damage in 1973 which permitted the escape of fish from the Little Marsh and the smaller units. I believe most of the increased eagle use during the 1973-74 winter can be attributed to the easy pickings from stranded fish as the flood waters receded.

Charles R. Darling, Manager, Quivira NWR

Three bald eagles stayed around a pond one-half mile south and one-half mile east of the lake during the month of December, 1975. The pond was drying up, and fish (carp and bullheads) were stranded and dying. I observed bald eagles feeding there several times.

Robert J. Price, District Game Biologist, Lake McKinney WMA

When shad are available, they are utilized heavily by the eagles.

Lloyd B. Fox, District Game Biologist, Marais des Cygnes WMA

Wintering eagles on reservoirs do eat some fish but less here than on large rivers below large reservoirs.

R. E. McWhorter, Regional Game Supervisor, Tuttle Creek WMA

OKLAHOMA:

Salt content increases with rainfall severity and evaporation, and decreases with rainfall amount, i.e., sudden, severe rains wash the salt deposits from the salt flats into the lake while long, slow rains allow the salt to soak into the ground. Also, extended rains usually raise the lake enough to increase spillway flow as well as diluting the lake's concentration. Some of the changes are sudden, and low level fish kills are not uncommon.

Most of the lake (and all of the Salt Fork of the Arkansas River) is very shallow, which allows reasonable opportunity for eagles to take live fish.

Ronald S. Sullivan, Manager, Salt Plains NWR

ILLINOIS:

Swan Lake, a 2,000 acre shallow lake which is directly connected to the Illinois River, and Gilbert Lake, a 625 acre impoundment adjacent to the Illinois River, provide a food basic of fish, primarily gizzard shad.

> *Hugh H. Null, Manager, Swan & Gilbert Lakes District, Mark Twain NWR*

The extremely abundant Gizzard Shad, three to four inches in length, were the primary food of the eagles; but occasionally small carp and buffalo were taken. Throughout most of the winter, the open holes along the shore were literally choked with shad probably as a result of the intolerance of the species to reduced amounts of oxygen or to decreased temperatures as was reported for the American Shad. Many were dead or dying, and the live ones often swam near the surface or in a very shallow ater. The fish are relatively weak swimmers and were thus vulnerable when exposed to sudden changes in current. The result was an almost constant and readily available food supply for the eagles.

> *William E. Southern, Savanna Army Depot, Mississippi River, The Wilson Bulletin 75(1): page 46 (1963)*

Spring foods appear to be primarily winter-killed fish, both from the refuge and the Mississippi River. Fish account for a portion of the fall foods also.

> *Tom J. Early, Manager, Louisa & Keithsburg Districts, Mark Twain NWR*

During winter each year the gizzard shad population of the upper Mississippi is reduced tremendously. Shad are extremely susceptible to stress, and the low temperatures and decreased oxygen under snow covered ice are stress factors causing death of many of the weaker river fish. Fish of other species also succumb, but not in the numbers noted for shad. These dead fish then may become available to eagles in stretches of open water. The turbulent waters below dams remain open throughout the winter as well as industrially heated waters in certain areas. In addition, the turbulence of the water as it passes through the dam can serve as a factor causing the demise of fish already under stress from other factors. Naturally predators are attracted to areas of weakened and dead or dying fish. This includes predator fish as well as birds.

I have watched the eagles fish in the water below Lock and Dam 14, and I feel certain that these areas are extremely important to the birds' winter survival. Some commercial fishermen seining under the ice leave a portion of their catch on the ice for the eagles.

> *William A. Bertrand, Streams Project Fisheries, State Department of Conservation*

MISSOURI:

Food source most used by these birds is crippled waterfowl although dead fish are also sought after. In February, 1964, after a fish kill in an oxbow lake, 37 eagles were counted making use of the dead fish.

Noel G. Seek, Assistant Manager, Schell-Osage WMA, Missouri

The natural fishing resource may also be an attractant at this time since many species of fish including carp, crappie, bass, bluegill, shad, drum, catfish, bullhead, gar and various minnows are found in the refuge streams and water impoundments.

The typical winter open-water situation consists of open water throughout most of the winter months. There is usually a time period of less than a week or two when the water impoundments are frozen. During this freeze-up period, scattered areas remain open due to water-fowl activity in this area, wind (weather) conditions, and/or the area's habitat conditions. During freeze up waterfowl do congregate at these open water areas, and likewise so do the eagles in the area.

Gerald L. Clawson, Manager, Mingo NWR

On the Clarence Cannon Refuge this winter, the bald eagles fed on shad. Water bodies froze over December 17, however the eagles re-mained and fed on dead shad frozen at the top of the ice. The eagles re-mained until a blizzard hit the area December 26.

Glen R. Miller, Manager, Cannon and Delair Divisions, Mark Twain NWR

TENNESSEE:

Rapid, weather-related, water temperature changes occasionally re-sult in high mortality of threadfin and gizzard shad in certain reser-voirs; and a few eagles commonly occur in these areas. Concentrations of any injured fish in the tailwaters below many dams apparently attract wintering eagles.

Thomas H. Riley, Director, Division of Wildlife Development, TVA

LOUISIANA:

Birds congregate at Toledo Bend primarily because of the large fish population, particularly shad, and the availability of these fish after they pass through the generators of the hydroelectric plant.

S. Ray Aycock, Jr., Wildlife Biologist, U.S. Fish and Wildlife Service

MINNESOTA:

Most of the eagles sighted on the refuge are in the vicinity of Rice Lake where they appear to be attracted to the dead carp that are winter killed in the lake.

John E. Wilbrecht, Manager, Sherburne NWR

MONTANA:

Lake Helena is actually backwater from Hauser Lake, and it abounds with carp (there are many of them in the Missouri, also). Most of Lake

Helena freezes about Thanksgiving, and much of it is shallow.

Ice in Lake Helena usually is breaking up well by mid-March, and the word gets around among the eagles. A dozen on the lake and in the vicinity of it is not uncommon. Records which George Holton of the state Fish and Game Department keeps indicate that 5 to 14 frequented the lake during the springs of 1972-1976. Sid Martin, also of Helena, counted 36 on the lake one spring in the mid-1960's, and I found 52 a few years prior to that when water in Hauser Lake was lowered for repairs on the dam. Ice in Lake Helena broke out early as a result, and the eagles took advantage of it.

Mrs. William F. McKinney, Helena, Montana, Audubon Society

During the early spring buildup, the birds are obviously exploiting a harvest of dead fishes that emerge with the break up.

P. D. Skaar, Montana State University, Bozeman

SOUTH DAKOTA:

Eagles use several food soures in the general area. During late fall and early winter, the main food source is fish which the eagles pick up below Fort Randall Dam. Goldeneye, white bass, carp, walleye, gizzard shad, and paddlefish are observed food species. The white bass apparently pass through the power tunnels in the dam before the eagles get them. The carp have become available to the eagles when they have passed through the dam's flood tunnels. The goldeneye and paddlefish originate in the tailwaters. Gizzard shad winter die offs have provided an important food source for about a month.

Al Trout, Assistant Refuge Manager, Lake Andes NWR

We did have one concentration of thirteen bald eagles on Rush Lake, located 10 miles south of the Waubay NWR, feeding on winter killed fish in early April of 1972.

Robert R. Johnson, Manager, Waubay National Wildlife Refuge

"Bald Eagles are primarily scavengers, feeding on dead and dying fish. The wintering eagles often spend many hours perched in trees near open water. Most of this time is spent watching for dead fish to float by, and in preening the feathers of wings and tail. Dead fish such as gizzard shad, goldeneye and even gar found floating or lying along the shore line of rivers and below dams are commonly eaten. Occasionally other dead animals are also utilized for food."

Dr. Thomas C. Dunstan 1970
The Wintering Bald Eagle of South Dakota
South Dakota Conservation Digest 37(6): 12-15

IDAHO:

For several years we were experimentally reducing numbers of whitefish with explosives in the South Fork of the Snake River in the 40 miles just downstream from Palisades Dam. During these years as many as 90 bald and 10 golden eagles were counted at various times in late winter, apparently attracted to the area by the availability of dead whitefish. Normally, only about 15 eagles are sighted in a late-winter float trip down the South Fork.

Paul Jeppson, Idaho Dept. of Fish and Game

In Lakes Walcott and Milner, there are heavy populations of rough fish, particularly, suckers, carp, chubs, and lesser populations of catfish, trout, and perch that inhabit these waters. All of these waters remain ice-free over large areas during most of the wintering period.

Dan Poppleton, Conservation Officer, Idaho Fish & Game Department

UTAH:

In the spring the principal food base is carp that died during winter and are made available as the ice breaks in spring.

Ned I. Peabody, Manager, Bear River Migratory Bird Refuge

The main attraction is later in March when large numbers of dead carp are exposed when the ice starts to melt. These carp are trapped in the ice each year when waters within the diked areas are drained following the hunting season to prevent ice damage to the dikes.

Noland F. Nelson, Superintendent, Ogden Bay WMA

In January of 1975 I counted 58 bald eagles on the area feeding on carp that I had killed in the units. About 50 tons of carp were killed by letting salt water into the units from the Great Salt Lake.

Timothy H. Provan, Superintendent, Farmington Bay WMA

NEVADA:

Most are found on the west boundary of the refuge adjacent to the hatchery fish ponds. They find the small trout in these rearing ponds an available food source. Trout and bass are found throughout the marsh but are generally not available to eagles.

R. V. Papike, Manager, Ruby Lake NWR

10

Carrion Utilized by Bald Eagles

Carrion from livestock, big game animals, and trapper discards is the buffer food supply that makes many a bald eagle wintering ground successfully habitable. Although mammalian carrion is low on the bald eagles' food preference scale, this does not diminish the essential role it plays during critical freeze-up periods. In fact, there are groups of eagles that rely almost solely on mammalian carrion to carry them through the winter. For example, the 10 to 12 bald eagles wintering on ice-locked Quabbin Reservoir in Massachusetts have little else but deer carcasses upon which to feed. Throughout the Western United States, carrion likewise plays a major role in supporting the bald eagle population.

Road and hunter-killed game animals, while relatively common, are so dispersed that bald eagles utilizing them necessarily are ranging widely, either as single individuals or very small groups of 2 to 3. This floating winter population is hard to tally. Only an unpredictable windfall like the fish kill on a shallow 10-15 acre lake in northeast New Mexico, that for a brief period pulls in more bald eagles than there was any knowledge of in the area, are we alerted to the extent of rangeland foraging.

MINNESOTA:

After the inland lakes freeze over, the birds feed on carrion. They are frequently (once or twice a year or more) observed feeding on highway-killed deer. There are newspaper articles of eagles being captured in coyote traps. Winter sets are baited with meat scraps or carrion. A few beaver trappers report feeding eagles (birds on their territory) beaver carcasses in March and early April.

William E. Taylor, Wildlife Biologist, Hiawatha National Forest

WISCONSIN:

Their main diet is fish. However, during severly cold weather when there are only small open water areas present, eagles can be seen up to 15 miles inland, where they feed on dead farm animals and small animals.

Robert E. Wilson, Manager, Cassville District, Upper Mississippi River NWR

Third source of lesser importance is miscellaneous carrion, particularly muskrat carcasses discarded by trappers.

Kenneth O. Butts, Manager, La Crosse District, Upper Mississippi River NWR

NORTH DAKOTA:

Fall migration of bald eagles occurs during the deer season, and I suspect the number of eagles on the refuge is related to the number of deer killed and gut piles available for food.

David C. McGlauchlin, Manager, Audubon NWR

SOUTH DAKOTA:

Food habitats shift to carrion when it becomes available later on in the winter and eagle populations shift from the river to the upland areas. Eagles begin roosting at Lake Andes at that time. Ducks, geese, pheasants, and rabbits are the major food source of eagles using the upland areas.

Al Trout, Assistant Refuge Manager, Lake Andes NWR

Eagles began using upland areas shortly after Lake Francis Case froze (January 12, 1974-75; December 15, 1975-76). There was a corresponding shift in food habits at those times. It is my opinion that upland habitat is more important for wintering bald eagles than we had previously thought.

Karen Steenhof, Research Biologist, Lake Andes NWR

KANSAS:

When the crippled waterfowl are depleted, the eagles move to the cattle feedlots in the area. I counted 15 bald eagles in the trees around S & H Feeders south of Ellinwood, Kansas. This is about 12 air miles southeast of the center of Cheyenne Bottoms. Hoards of red-winged blackbirds and starlings descend on the feedlot each day to utilize the abundant grain supply. The feedlots must use a good deal of poison for the blackbirds and starlings, because there are always a lot of dead birds around. Therefore, I believe the bald eagles utilize the easily obtainable starlings and blackbirds when the crippled waterfowl are depleted.

After a discussion of the possibility of secondary poisoning of eagles with a U.S. Game Agent, I watched the S & H Feedlot throughout the month of February. I saw no actual instance of an eagle picking up a blackbird or starling. However, I feel that they must be utilizing these birds as a food source. During this time I found no dead or sick eagles.

In addition to the bald eagles around the feedlot, I saw an abundance of golden eagles, march hawks, ferruginous hawks, and rough-legged hawks.

   Bob Bartels, District Game Biologist, Cheyenne Bottoms WMA

My only observations of eagles feeding in the sandhills (bald eagles) were of eagles feeding on dead cattle, skinned coyote carcasses, and jackrabbits caught in coyote traps.

   Robert J. Price, District Game Biologist, Lake McKinney WMA

I have had two trappers tell me that they have had trouble with eagles damaging coyote pelts when they set gas guns for coyotes in sandhill areas.

I have seen eagles dive down on coyotes pulling out of dive just seconds from hitting coyote. I was unable to tell if the coyote might have been carrying anything in its mouth. Coyotes didn't like the eagles' action. Often I have seen them head for a fence. They would then continue on their way next to the fence.

It is my belief that these birds must have a rough time getting enough to eat. I know that they must eat whatever is available.

   Bruce C. Peters, District Game Protector, Lakin, Kansas

OKLAHOMA:

The eagles do feed on carcasses of bison and elk when available on the Wichita Mountains Wildlife Refuge. They also feed on the offal from elk taken during our December hunt period.

   Gene Bartnicki, Wildlife Management Biologist

In Osage County (Oklahoma) bald eagles fed primarily on cattle carcasses. Nine eagles were observed feeding on a single carcass. A feedlot owner north of Grainola, Oklahoma, stated 10 eagles fed regularly on cattle carcasses in a lot adjacent to his home. Whenever large concentrations of eagles were seen in Osage County, carcasses of cattle were nearby.

James W. Lish, MS Thesis, (1975) Oklahoma State University

We are in an area of great open, undeveloped land. Primarily ranching, rather sparse habitation of humans. I would say that except for large impoundments of water, the eagle has much the same environment for a 30 mile radius that existed 100 years ago, probably lots more carrion for now there is the cow and great herds of deer that did not exist in such numbers back then.

Frank Bunch, Goddard Youth Camp, Sulphur, Oklahoma

COLORADO:

The most common food for bald eagles in this area in the winter is road-killed deer which are shared with golden eagles, black-billed magpies, and ravens.

James W. Packard, Superintendent, Curecanti National Recreation Area, National Park Service

UTAH:

The other feeding area for bald eagles is the Gordon Creek Wildlife Management Area in Carbon County. This area is about 10 miles west of Price, Utah. It is an excellent wintering area for Mule Deer. A good population of blacktail jackrabbits and cottontail rabbits inhabits this area. The ecotypes of this area are pinion-juniper, cultivated fields— primarily alfalfa and sagebrush-grasslands. As I recall, nine bald eagles—three adult and six juveniles—were observed feeding on three deer carcasses during mid-December of 1975 in Gordon Creek.

Larry B. Dalton, Wildl, Biol., State Div. of Wildl. Resources

UTAH:

In Rush and Cedar Valleys, Utah, some use is made of various types of carrion. Both species of eagles have been seen feeding at carcasses of winter-killed sheep which are plentiful (40,000 sheep are present at one time or another during the winter). Hair from the mule deer has appeared in pellets, presumably from carrion. Road-killed rabbits may be eaten at times, as was a road-killed domestic cat. Many thousands of rabbits are shot and left each year by recreational hunters, which contributes a tremendous volume of food to carnivores and scavengers.

Clyde C. Edwards, PhD Thesis 1969, Brigham Young University

MONTANA:

These birds feed on dead and dying fish, waterfowl, and deer carcasses. I have found as many as four bald eagles feeding on one deer carcass. Trapper discards are readily utilized by bald eagles. Many times bald eagles steal food from successful golden eagles. Bald eagles are mainly scavengers.

Terrence P. McEneaney, Biologist Technician, U.S. Fish & Wildlife Service, Sheridan, Wyoming

Last year many ranchers lost large numbers of newborn calves out on the range due to a severe late spring storm. This was last spring. Our neighbor, who ranches near the base of the Sweetgrass Hills, observed four adult bald eagles feeding on the dead calves for about three weeks. I also observed them flying over Chester coming from the Marias River area heading north to the hills to feed.

People who live below Tiber Reservoir and vicinity have observed the eagles feeding on ducks in the Marias River below the Tiber Reservoir since there is always open water below the reservoir. Based on all of the observations made over the years, it appears a few bald eagles winter in the area described above.

Marvin E. Krook, Chester, Montana

Eagles were also seen in the Swan Lake area feeding on deer carcasses this winter. There are a large number of deer killed by cars and trucks along Highway 209 between Swan Lake and Seeley Lake each winter.

Wanda Jamieson, Secretary, Lower Flathead Valley Bird Club

The most interesting story of both balds and goldens has come to me twice from different people and from different mountain ridges. A deer that has been killed by a mountain lion or a pack of coyotes seems to attract both kinds of eagles, no matter where it is. They will come in and gorge themselves so that they cannot take off from the ground where the carrion is. Twice, friends of mine have seen the golden and the bald struggle up the ridge on foot to a point high enough for a take-off. Flying is necessarily slow, but they seem to know how to take off for home above the valleys where they need not lift their excess weight.

Miss Urana Clarke, Livingston, Montana Audubon Society

IDAHO:

Groups of eagles are occasionally seen on a big game carcass, but generally they are scattered along the river. Much of their food consists of carrion which includes waterfowl, big game carcasses and fish left by river otter. I would guess that carrion supplies the major portion of their winter diet. They will hunt big game carrion 5 to 10 miles from major river systems.

Walter L. Bodie, Regional Game Biologist, Idaho Department of Fish & Game

During the winter of 72-73, the upper Snake River (above Blackfoot, Idaho) was frozen over more extensively and longer than normal. About 30 bald eagles wintered at Camas Refuge Headquarters. They probably were feeding on mallards and pheasants although we did not see the evidence I would expect with that many eagles. The jackrabbits were down to nearly zero, following a spectacular peak during the winter of 70-71. Balds did feed on jackrabbits there to some extent.

Larry H. Worden, Mgr., Humboldt Bay NWR

A bald eagle was observed feeding on road-killed jackrabbits south of Malta, Idaho

Dan Poppleton, Conservation Officer, Idaho Fish & Game Department

Bald eagles are frequently observed during the winter feeding on deer carcasses from animals that have fallen through, or died on, the ice at Lucky Peak and Arrowrock Reservoirs.

James F. Keating, Regional Supervisor, Idaho Fish & Game Department

OREGON:

During the past two winters, the number of wintering birds has increased. This is thought to be due to the reduced numbers of deer killed on the highway about 40 miles to the northwest of this area. When the deer are numerous on the winter range, many animals are killed each year and this along with the rodents, mostly rabbits, that are also killed on the highway, constitute the main food supply of these birds. When the numbers of deer and rabbits are down, the birds move into this area to feed on the crippled and dead waterfowl that results from the hunting season on the management area.

A. B. Claggett, Manager, Summer Lake WMA, Oregon

WASHINGTON:

The rabbits (same species as that which overran Australia, New Zealand, England, and other areas) were probably introduced onto San Juan Island in the 1880's or earlier.

Rabbit densities reach 200 hectare. Probably, on the other San Juan Islands, the eagles feed on the usual native and livestock carrion. Here on San Juan Island, they enjoy the best of two possible worlds: marine-oriented food sources and rabbits.

Normally, island eagles will scavenge road-killed rabbits or natural mortalities when possible. Very frequently, robbing occurs. On many occasions, I have observed both red-tails and golden eagles being robbed by bald eagles. I estimate that each red-tail (probably the most efficient predator on rabbits) preying in open areas must kill two rabbits for each it is "allowed" for itself.

Actual bald eagle predation on rabbits occurs infrequently. But, in an average winter day, I observed several (3-5) attempted predations by immature eagles on live rabbits. Very few attempts are successful (2 percent ?); eagle experience or lack thereof is an unquantified factor

in rabbit predation. But, the fact that some are consistently successful is significant. Adult bald eagles, which seem to rely much less on
rabbits than do immatures, are not often seen to attempt active predation.

William Stevens, National Park Service, San Juan Island

In addition, eagles were observed to feed on black-tail deer, cows,
coyotes, and other prey. All were taken as carrion, not by killing. I've
noticed a larger dependence on these supplementary food sources during times of flooding, heavy snowfall, and especially towards the later
part of the winter when most of the salmon carcasses are used up. One
deer carcass was observed to attract up to 50 percent of the population.

*Mark Stalmaster, Graduate Student, Huxley College of Environ-
mental Studies*

When, as the result of high (flood) water along the Skagit, 20 February 1975, stranded and dead salmon became unavailable, a group of
14 bald eagles and 10 ravens were observed around the carcass of a
deer that apparently had gone untouched by the eagles for several
months.

Christopher Servheen, MS Thesis, Univ. of Washington (1975)

ALASKA:

At least 25 active areas were located, even though the southern coastline was not completely surveyed. Bald eagles were concentrated particularly in winter near the refuse dumping areas, 130 birds were
counted on 27 December 1970.

G. V. Byrd (et al) in "Birds of Adak Island, Alaska."
The Condor 76(4): 472-476, winter 1974

BRITISH COLUMBIA:

The most prominent food item in the diet of the wintering eagles in
the study area is dead sheep. All of the large concentrations of eagles
were associated with sheep carcasses. For example, on 27 February 14
adults and 15 immatures were observed perched around one 200-acre
field containing three partially eaten sheep carcasses. Usually only one
bird would feed at a time while two or three more would be perched on
nearby rocks and fence posts. Over the past six years, the local sheep
rancher and myself have spent hundreds of hours observing these
eagles from blinds. Never once have we witnessed an attack or attempted attack by an eagle on young lambs or on ewes giving birth.

Sidney and Moresby Islands both had temporarily high concentrations of eagles associated with sheep carcasses. Once the carcasses
were consumed, the eagles dispersed. On the other hand, San Juan
Island regularly supports a large wintering eagle population. This
island is unique in that rabbits, in addition to sheep, are important
food items.

*David Hancock from: "Bald Eagles Wintering in the Southern Gulf
Islands, British Columbia*

11

Feeding Behavior

From the status of a fiercely independent provider during the nesting season to semi-cooperative hunting on the wintering grounds is quite a step. However, the social existence in winter may have survival value for the immatures. There appears to be a carry-over from the fledgling period, as immature birds continue to "insist" that adults turn over their catch to them, even when food is easily obtained. Later the dwindling food supply progressively develops competitive skills, for now any bald eagle succeeding in catching prey must be prepared to either elude, or defend itself against, other eagles. Squabbling over prey becomes the order of the day.

Cooperative hunting is perhaps too generous a term to apply to a group of bald eagles standing like so many herdsmen on the ice at the perimeter of a dense flock of waterfowl, or perched in trees and on fence posts about an open field in which geese are feeding. At intervals individual eagles take off to haze the geese into flight. But when a laggard goose is isolated and brought down (or a sick goose located), then the entire group will attempt to share the prey—even to waiting perched nearby for their turn.

There is certainly an advantage in having several birds perched and others in the air about a field when a rabbit breaks cover, as described by Edwards. An expert at quick turns, the rabbit has a better than even chance of eluding a lone eagle whose air brakes in low, level flight don't respond that quickly. It is quite understandable that a number of bald eagles can feed concurrently from a carcass of a deer, cow, or even sheep. Even a raven or gull can snatch a quick morsel. But I find it difficult to visualize a successful eagle with a rabbit sharing such small prey with hunting companions without putting up a struggle for sole possession.

117

These winter aggregations of bald eagles may be somewhat like an unorganized crowd, ready and willing to seize any advantage disclosed by the more aggressive individuals among them.

The winter-migrant bald eagle thrusts itself into areas where resident carnivor and scavenger are already utilizing foods the eagle expects to appropriate. These competitors (coyote, fox, crow, magpie, gull, vulture, hawks and owls) tend to give way to any determined demand of the bald eagle. In fact, the bald eagle is not above forcing other raptors to give up the prey they are more adept at catching. For example, William Steven's account of how bald eagles obtain rabbits on San Juan Island says, "I estimate that each Red-tailed Hawk (Possibly the most efficient predator on rabbits) preying in open areas must kill two rabbits for each it is "allowed" to keep for itself." Nevertheless, the resident competitors for the often scarce winter foods can severely limit the "visitor load" an area can accommodate.

MONTANA:

Birds of prey characteristically form pellets which are regurgitated some time after feeding. At no time were pellets found during this study (feeding on spawned-out salmon). I believe that fish bones are readily digested by bald eagles.

Young birds often attempt to steal fish, either from other immatures or from adults, by chasing them in flight or by flying directly at a perched bird in an attempt to make it drop the fish. They were often quite successful at this.

Immature birds were more prone to secure fish along the stream edges, either by landing and picking up fish which had been washed ashore or by wading into shallow water and picking up dead fish off the bottom with their talons.

Chases were especially common near the end of the salmon spawning when fish were scarce. Great aerial agility was often shown during these chases. On a number of occasions, mature birds were observed stealing fish by flying under another bird from the rear, flipping over to an upside down position, and plucking the fish from the other's talons. A more frequent tactic was to keep diving on the successful bird until it dropped the fish.

Occasionally when a bird was sitting on a perch eating a fish, another bird, again often a young one, would dive on it with outstretched talons to make the first one drop the fish. On a few occasions, the feeding bird would literally be knocked off its perch and into the water; and the fish would be lost to both as it sanked to the bottom.

David S. Shea, MS Thesis, University of Montana, 1973

IDAHO:

The competition for food in the winter of 1974-75 was very low, and instances of physical confrontations during food procurement were rare. In 1975-76 the situation was quite the reverse as on many occasions one could observe up to three eagles pursuing another eagle that had successfully captured a fish. This chase often resulted in the original captor dropping the salmon, and one of the pursuers retaking the fish. The available food supply also led to a wider distribution of the eagles than last year, thus eliminating the common sight of a large group of eagles congregating in any one area as in the 1974-75 period.

Joseph B. Lint, Wildlife Biologist, Bureau of Land Management, Coeur d'Alene

ILLINOIS:

Wading in shallow water and catching fish with the beak. This method was used along the shore of the main channel, its backwaters, and the running water of Crooked Slough. It was the most successful manner of feeding. Adult eagles, and occasionally immatures, waded up to their bellies in water and characteristically submerged their heads when capturing fish. I watched one adult capture and swallow at least ten shad, head end first, in two minutes. The eagles were most wary while in this situation. Sometimes the body and flight feathers were so wet that the bird had difficulty taking flight.

William E. Southern, Savanna Army Depot, Mississippi River
The Wilson Bulletin 75(1): p. 47 (1963)

OKLAHOMA:

When the reservoir (Salt Plains) was ice covered, most feeding by the common merganser was done below the dam where large schools of gizzard shad congregated... When a large school of shad was located, the birds became densely packed together. Merganser feeding activities were frequently interrupted by Ring-billed and Herring Gulls and *bald eagles*.

B. W. Anderson (et al), "Notes on the Feeding Behavior of the Common Merganser"
The Condor, 76(4): 472-476 winter 1974

Lish observed bald eagles attempting to capture Canada geese on at least five occasions in the winter of 1973-74. They perched on fence posts or trees around winter wheat fields where geese were feeding. The eagle flew directly toward the flock which took flight as the bird approached. Except when the bald eagle was able to pick out a crippled bird, the goose seemed very capable of out-flying the eagle in level flight.

James W. Lish, MS Thesis (1975), Oklahoma State University

TEXAS:

The bald eagles at Buffalo Lake NWR follow the large concentrations of waterfowl as they feed and loaf on the surrounding winter wheat fields and playa lakes. The eagles usually take only the sick or injured birds. On the refuge the eagles perch in the tall cottonwood trees located on the south end of the lake and fed on the ducks and geese as they loaf on the ice.

Larry Wynn, Buffalo Lake NWR, Umbarger, Texas

SOUTH DAKOTA:

It was observed that the young bald eagles were constantly trying to steal fish away from the talons of the mature bald eagles. This activity would take place both in flight and in the perches used during the day.

An observation was made by project personnel where an immature eagle either tried to catch too large a fish or misjudged his distance from the water. He went completely under the water and just about did not come back out. When finally airborne, he went to the nearest tree to hang his wings on the branches to dry.

Dale Lundquist, U.S. Corps of Engineers, Lake Francis Case

During February 1975, I noticed two bald eagles, one juvenile and one adult, flying around the switchyard southwest of the powerhouse, with the younger eagle clutching a fish. The adult eagle was harassing the juvenile by diving toward it, chasing it, and attempting to grab the fish away. The harassment went on about 5 minutes with both birds flying very close to the powerhouse and around the switchyard transmission towers. Finally, the young eagle dropped the fish, and the adult dived and caught it in mid-air. Both birds then left the area.

Bruce Short, U.S. Corps of Engineers, Lake Oahe

WASHINGTON:

Feeding on dead salmon washed up on gravel bars along the Skagit River usually occurred twice each day. Feeding was intensive until approximately 1000 hours, then might not be resumed until late afternoon about two hours before sunset. In the interim the eagles usually perch for several hours adjacent to the feeding area. It was not uncommon to observe an eagle perched in the same spot for 6 to 8 hours until the evening feeding period began. This routine was broken on sunny days when developing thermal updrafts permitted soaring.

Christopher Servheen, MS Thesis, University of Washington 1975

NOVA SCOTIA, CANADA:

The most commonly observed method appeared to be that of wading in shallow water, particularly in the Big Harbour Islands and Boom Island Region of River Denys Basin. A fish was grasped by one talon and dragged ashore to be eaten.

Edward Francis Gittens, MS Thesis, Acadia University 1968

BRITISH COLUMBIA:

On 22 January 300 widgeon and teal were flushed out of the shallow water by the airplane. Immediately one adult and two immature eagles were observed attacking a crippled widgeon. Seventeen passes were made in rapid succession by the three eagles, and each time the widgeon dove to safety creating considerable spray. When the eagles tired and returned to perches, the widgeon swam from the shallow to deeper water. This pattern of activity was repeated several times throughout the winter, with usually three or four eagles working simultaneously at one duck.

From: "Bald Eagles Wintering in the Southern Gulf Islands, British Columbia"
By: David Hancock

UTAH:

As the lake "iced over," waterfowl concentrated in one area in order to keep the water open. The bald eagles would then move out onto the ice and maintain a constant vigilance over their prey. As the weather and ice conditions became more severe, the waterfowl numbers dwindled from 6,000 in November to nothing by early January of each year.

Larry B. Dalton, Wildlife Biologist, Desert Lake WMA, Utah

There is a tendency for the bald eagle to hunt more often in small groups and to cooperate in flushing and killing of prey. Hunting techniques consist of short coursing flights back and forth over vegetative cover concealing prey (jackrabbits). I have observed eagles to land and then walk along the ground through low brush in what appears to be deliberate attempts to flush prey. With some birds always nearby in the air, any prey flushed is often dispatched rather quickly. From observation and evidence of wing marks in the snow, it appears that half of the rabbits flushed are killed in not over 30 meters if two or more birds are cooperating.

Clyde C. Edwards, PhD Thesis 1969, Brigham Young University

KANSAS:

In the ten years I have been working for the Game Commission, I have seen eagles chase many ducks at Lake McKinney. Some of these chases lasted four minutes. The duck would soon tire of the flight and then begin to fly very close to top of water. The eagles did not seem to like this low level flight over water. I have seen ducks on occasion dive into the water.

Bruce C. Peters, District Game Protector, Lakin, Kansas

At other times waterfowl are utilized. The bald eagles periodically fly over the waterfowl concentrations and get most of the birds up. When a cripple or sick bird is located, the eagles will center their attention on that bird. Often there will be three or more eagles on snags around a sick bird before an actual attempt is made by one of the eagles.

Lloyd B. Fox, District Game Biologist, Marais des Cygnes WMA

The eagles at Glen Elder WMA regularly use areas of flooded timber located in the two major river forks and Mill, Walnut and Granite Creeks as perches while hunting. It was also observed that the eagles concentrated in areas where an ice shelf was present; hazed the ducks and would capture weaker birds on the ice shelf. When warm weather and high winds broke up the ice shelf in one area, the eagles would move to another area where there was ice. Apparently, sick or crippled ducks were more readily caught on the ice than in open water where they could dive to escape.

Donald R. Roy & Ken Tompkins, Game Biologist, Kansas State

12

Communal Roosts of the Bald Eagle

Communal roosts at night are a unique characteristic of the migrant bald eagle in its wintering area. Even in areas where there is no dearth of perches, the birds may choose to crowd together in one tree, commonly accompanied by much dispute and juggling for position. James Lish, near the Salt Fork of the Arkansas River in Oklahoma, observed 61 of the 111 bald eagles using a particular night roost perched in one dead cottonwood.

Although some night roosts are in close proximity to the feeding area, this is not an essential requirement. In areas like Lake Coeur d'Alene in Idaho, there would appear to be no necessity to move very far from the feeding area. On the other hand, the complete lack of tree cover in the marshes of Great Salt Lake in Utah can well account for the daily one-way commuting of 10 to 15 miles to forested sites well up on the mountain slopes.

Factors other than commuting distance are obviously very important, freedom from human disturbances, for example. But even this is not absolute for major roosts are located within a mile of a traveled highway, are surrounded by croplands, or experience periodic livestock operations.

Weather is certainly a factor, and some over-wintering aggregations of bald eagles have alternate night roosts whose use depends on the severity of temperature and storm.

Several observers have suggested that the selection of the night roost site is governed by atmospheric conditions bearing on the dynamics of flight from the roost in the hour before dawn.

Important as are these night roosting sites, the failure to preserve a specific site does not necessarily mean losing the eagles wintering in that general area. For example, Ron Sullivan reports that bald eagles wintering on Salt Plains National Wildlife Refuge in Oklahoma have lost two night roosting sites in recent years and are now relocated on a third. Food is the lodestone.

The specific perching site at the night roost is almost invariably a tree protruding above the general forest canopy, permitting both an unobstructed approach and takeoff. Freedom from a maize of small branches often makes a dead tree or snag the perch-of-choice, although its perpetuation-in-time is limited.

As much as a half hour before sunrise, eagles begin streaming out of the roost heading for feeding areas, not to return until dusk. However, the roost is seldom completely vacated, in fact, inclement weather may cause most of the eagles to remain perched throughout the day.

ILLINOIS:

On the Mississippi River, opposite Keokuk, Iowa, and below Lock and Dam No. 19, is The Nature Conservancy's "Cedar Glen Eagle Roost." An eroded area in Keokuk limestone forms a four-acre bowl with walls 75 to 100 feet tall. Oak trees grow on the top of these walls surrounding the bowl with sycamore trees growing in the bottom that provides a sheltered night roost during cold weather. According to Dr. Tom Dunstan, Western Illinois University, the population of bald eagles using this roost in the winter of 1972-73 was 98, in 1973-74 numbered 180, and in 1974-75 was 171.

On nights that are not quite so cold (freezing to 10 degrees below) the bald eagles will roost in the tall cottonwoods and silver maple on Mink Island and adjacent mainland.

Dr. Thomas C. Dunstan, Proceedings of Bald Eagle Days 1975

Pere Marquette State Park is located on the Illinois River just north of its confluence with the Mississippi River. Just across the Illinois River is Swan Lake, which is the most prominent feature in the 5,050 acre Calhoun Division of the Mark Twain National Wildlife Refuge. There are two major roosts in Pere Marquette State Park. Two hollows contain the major winter roost areas, Graham's Hollow and William's Hollow. William's Hollow is wide and tends up in an easterly direction then turning into a north-south ravine. The roost areas are located in the north and northeast slopes at the tops of these ravines. All roost trees are large living trees with their lower limbs below the crest of the ravine. The feeding areas are close by along the Illinois River and on Swan Lake.

The number of eagles in the area has fluctuated considerably. The largest count at the William's Hollow roost site was 62 birds in late February, 1970.

Richard Bowes, Proceedings of Bald Eagle Days 1975

While studying wintering bald eagles in the Cassville, Wisconsin area, Terrence Ingram discovered that in the evening the birds that had been feeding just below Lock and Dam No. 10 on the Mississippi River headed north to an overnight roost some 7 miles distance. This roosting area was subsequently acquired by a southwest Wisconsin conservation group, Eagle Valley Environmentalists, Inc. Eagle Valley is three miles long and parallels the Mississippi River. The steep 350 bluffs form more of a canyon than a valley, are heavily forested, and hosts 40 to 50 bald eagles on a winter's night.

Terrence N. Ingram, Executive Director, Eagle Valley Environmentalists, Inc.

OKLAHOMA:

Located within a distance of approximately 15 miles along the Salt Fork of the Arkansas River in northcentral Oklahoma are five separate communal night roosts of the wintering bald eagle.

Roosts A and B are each surrounded by 64 hectares of cattle pasture. Both are 0.5 kilometer from the Salt Fork River, and a 0.5 kilometer from the nearest county road. Both are under the same private owner-ship. Hunting or trespassing is not permitted by the landowner, and disturbance due to livestock management in winter is minimal. A maximum of 120 bald eagles used Roosts A and B during the winters of 1973-74 and 1974-75.

Roost C is the third largest roost in the intensive study area. A maxi-mum of 70 eagles roosted here in the winter of 1973-74. Land use in the 64 hectares surrounding this roost is devoted to winter wheat. Human disturbance is minimal. The private landowner does not allow hunting or trespassing, and his attitude toward eagles is very favorable. Roost C is approximately 0.5 kilometer from the Salt Fork River and 1 kilo-meter from a state highway. The highway has no apparent effect on the eagles using this roost.

Roost D is located on Salt Plains National Wildlife Refuge adjacent to a small impoundment designed for waterfowl management. The trees are an even age stand of cottonwoods 30 to 40 meters in height. At least 36 bald eagles used this roost in the winter of 1974-75.

Roost E is much smaller than the roosts mentioned previously. On 2 January 1975, 11 bald eagles were present in cottonwoods fringing a small tributary of the Salt Fork River 200 meters north of a county road. The main roost tree is a dead cottonwood approximately 60 meters in height. Topography is flat. Winter wheat fields border the roost on two sides.

The preferred tree in Roost A is dead, taller than most trees in the roost. . . there are no small branches to obstruct an eagle when land-ing. Sixty-one of the 111 eagles at Roost A perched in this one tree the evening of 22 December 1973. Eagles perched in a linear arrangement along a limb usually were only about 50 centimeters apart.

James William Lish, MS Thesis, Oklahoma State University 1975

Bald eagles wintering on the Salt Plains National Wildlife Refuge have been forced (through loss of roosting trees) to change sites at least twice in recent years.

Ron Sullivan, Manager, Salt Plains NWR

The small communal roost of wintering bald eagles near Comanche Lake on the Wichita Mountains National Wildlife Refuge has been known at least since 1940.

Gene Bartnicki, Wildlife Management Biologist, Wichita Mountains NWR

UTAH:

The eagles do range out of Ogden Bay. Most leave the management area to roost along the Weber River in large cottonwood trees 1 to 3 miles to the east.

Noland F. Nelson, Superintendent, Ogden Bay WMA, Utah

Information about their night roosting habits is very sketchy. Sightings in the marsh at dusk seem to indicate a few roost on rat houses. The majority are believed to fly to trees bordering the valley. There is some indication that a large number of birds catch wind currents and climb to great heights then fly to the trees high in the mountains for roosting.

> *Rodney F. Krey, Asst. Mgr., Bear River Migratory Bird Refuge*

They would leave Farmington Bay, Great Salt Lake, in the evening and fly into the nearby canyons to roost.

> *Timothy H. Provan, Superintendent, Farmington Bay WMA, Utah*

Above snow line in Willard Canyon, elevation 7,500 feet and 15.5 miles from Bear River Migratory Bird Refuge, 16 adults and one immature bald eagle roosted in a single large dead Douglas fir. On March 29th this roosting area was almost devoid of eagles. Eagle pellets were scattered profusely throughout the entire area. Approximately 90 percent contained duck feathers.

> *John F. Swisher, Jr., Bear River Migratory Bird Refuge, Wilson Bulletin 76: 186-187*

Two valley roosts of bald eagles were located near Fairfield and Vernon, Utah. Both were near farm corrals and homes. The rancher at the Fairfield site performed daily chores in close proximity to the tree in which the eagles were roosting. He was tolerated much closer than another man stranger to the area.

The Tintic and Oquirrh Mountain roosts were located in side canyons, north exposure and at an elevation of about 6,000 feet, which is 1,200 feet above the valley floor. The perching trees, Douglas fir, are located near the top of the ridge. A favorite tree may hold as many as 20 to 25 eagles before nearby trees are used.

> *Clyde C. Edwards, Ph.D. Thesis, Brigham Young University (1969)*

Bald eagles have a roost site in a medium-sized cottonwood tree about one-fourth mile northeast of the Desert Lake Waterfowl Management Area (WMA) in Emery County. Seven bald eagles, 2 adults and 5 juveniles, occupied this site in November, 1975. At any time of any day after arrival, these bald eagles could be observed in the roost or perched on top of muskrat lodges bordering the lake.

> *Larry B. Dalton, Wildl, Biol., Utah Div. Wildl. Resources*

WISCONSIN:

A wintering roost of the bald eagle was located on the Wisconsin River by the members of Eagle Valley Environmentalists who began the slow and arduous task of raising the money to purchase this site. By small gifts and the efforts of many school children, a bank account was accumulating. At this point the National Wildlife Federation threw its weight behind the program, and with funds provided by Anheuser-Bush, Inc. purchased a 150 acre forested tract incorporating the eagle roost. Named Ferry Bluff Bald Eagle Sanctuary, the management was assigned to the local organization who originated the program, Eagle Valley Environmentalists, Inc.

This year (1976) 26 bald eagles were actually observed using this roost, although almost twice that number of birds are in the Sauk City, Wisconsin, area. The main feeding area is about 5 miles upstream from Ferry Bluffs near the dam at Prairie du Sac, Wisconsin.

Patrick Peckham, EVE Coordinator for Ferry Bluffs

IDAHO:

In the Wolf Lodge Bay area, many perching sites and potential roosting sites occurred near the feeding area. However, the eagles did not spend the night at the feeding area, but flew to a communal night roosting site approximately 1.5 miles east of Beauty Bay. This area was utilized during days of calm or inclement weather.

Selected trees within a five-acre area were utilized for roosting. The area, being quite steep, and snow-covered, provided a relatively isolated roosting area. The preferred roost trees were those western white pine and western larch which extended above the canopy.

On warm or windy days, the eagles did not spend the night at the above roost area. Instead, near dusk they would drift out of sight over the ridges to the south of Wolf Lodge Bay and presumably travel to an alternate roost area at a higher elevation in the Coeur d'Alene National Forest.

Joseph B. Lint, Wildl. Biol., Bur. Land Mgmt., Coeur d'Alene

SOUTH DAKOTA:

During the periods of upland hunting for carrion from livestock and game animals, eagles roosted in a small stand of trees on the bank of Lakes Andes National Wildlife Refuge.

Karen Steenhof, Research Biologist, Lake Andes NWR

KANSAS:

Eagles roost in timber on the Lake McKinney shoreline and do in milder weather. When it gets rough, they usually winter in the River Bottom about 1 to 1.5 miles south of the lake.

In Hamilton County on the river, I know of a roost site about 6 miles east of Syracuse. This area has good mature cottonwood trees on the south bank of river next to sand hills. Eagles usually arrive in October-November and most are seen in December. This roost contains 12 to 15 birds that are usually all bald eagles.

Another roost is located between the river bottom and sand hills about 2 miles east of Kendall in Kearny County. The roost is in heavy mature cottonwood trees and shelters about 25 to 35 birds with 10 to

15 being bald eagles. It was fairly well protected four years ago, but now a road goes right through it.

    Bruce C. Peters, District Game Protector, Lakin, Kansas

The sand hills immediately south of the Arkansas River in southwest Kansas are studded with windmills that provide roosts; and many of these are used by bald eagles, though golden eagles predominate.

    Robert J. Price, District Game Biologist, Lake McKinney WMA, Kansas

An outstanding feature about Cheney Reservoir, other than the available shad, would be that there are several stands of large cottonwood trees left standing in the water 100 yards or more from the shoreline when the lake was constructed. This offers the birds a reasonably secure roosting area, which they readily take advantage of.

    Ken Garrigues, Manager, Cheney WMA, Kansas

MONTANA:

In Glacier National Park, the most conspicuous and important roosting area is adjacent to the southwest shore of Lake McDonald, about 2 air miles from the feeding area. Here large black cottonwoods right along the lakeshore and tall western larches located 0.5 miles inland from the lake, provide the favorite perches. Another important roost is on the west bank of the Middle Fork about 0.7 miles south of the outlet of McDonald Creek. Proximity to water does not seem to be the major requirement as many birds spend the night quite a distance from it.

    David S. Shea, McDonald Creek, Glacier National Park

WASHINGTON:

One of several night roosts located along the Skagit River was on a south-facing ridge approximately 1,500 feet above the floor of the valley. Here throughout the 1973-74 season, 20 to 30 eagles roosted at night in a group of 12 to 15 dead conifers.

    Christopher Servheen, MS Thesis, University of Washington (1975)

CALIFORNIA:

A major aggregation of bald eagles find winter-long feeding at Lower Klamath and Tule Lake National Wildlife Refuges. The overnight roosting area lies 10 to 12 miles away on the Klamath National Forest in Siskiyou County, California, known as "Davis Road Bald Eagle Winter Roost." It is atypical in a sense, for while there is a favored grove of mature pine in which large numbers of eagles roost, birds can be observed perched here and there in tall pines scattered about an open brush-covered area of 6,400 acres. Forest biologists have counted 91 bald eagles, but the total numbers may well exceed 100 birds.

    Larry A. Forbis, Forest Wildlife Biologist, Kalamath National Forest, Yreka, California

13

Sanctuaries for Winter-Migrant Bald Eagles

In the last 5 to 6 years a new series of sanctuaries have come into being, specifically to protect roosting and feeding areas of winter migrant bald eagles. The emphasis at present is in acquiring from private ownership wooded tracts that serve as night roosts, and wooded fringe of feeding areas that serve as perching and loafing areas during the day. This activity is largely concentrated in the upper Mississippi River basin where local conservation needs are concurrently served.

These sanctuaries for wintering birds supplement a growing system of refuges to protect nesting raptors, including the bald eagle—a system involving any number of Federal land management agencies. For example, the U.S. Forest Service has the Chippewa Bald Eagle Nesting Area in Minnesota, Crane Prairie in Oregon, Eagle Lake in California, and Seymour Eagle Management Area in southeast Alaska. The Bureau of Land Management has the Snake River Birds of Prey Natural Area in Idaho, and the National Park Service its San Juan Island to name a few specific locations.

These programs are new only in the sense that protection of wintering bald eagles (or raptors in general) were the specific objective. Nevertheless, the far flung National Wildlife Refuge system has for many years been performing this very service of protecting habitats that the eagles could use to advantage—some 34 million acres. Combine this with the wildlife management areas under State administration—again in excess of 30 million acres, plus the National and State Park Systems, the Wilderness and Primitive areas on National Forests, the wild and scenic river's program, and the creation of over 1,500 large reservoirs with a surface area in excess of 14 million acres. All told it would seem that the bald eagle is not—with local exception—hard pressed for wintering grounds.

131

ILLINOIS:

Prairie State Eagle Refuge (In The Making)

The Conservancy's Illinois Chapter is involved in an innovative and successful program called a "Bicentennial Celebration for Illinois Students." It was initiated to help save the American bald eagle. Students throughout the state are being asked to participate in the celebration by each contributing at least ten cents towards the purchase of land to create a bald eagle refuge in Illinois.

The program is being jointly sponsored by the Illinois Department of Conservation, the Illinois Audubon Society, and the Conservancy's Illinois Chapter.

The "Bicentennial Celebration for Illinois Students" was conceived after the Illinois Chapter saw an immediate need to preserve at least 600 acres of habitat along the Mississippi River in Hancock County at an initial cost approaching $250,000.

The most exciting aspect of the program, however, is its success. As of March 4, approximately one month after the effort began, over $50,000 had been raised.

Pere Marquette Eagle Roost

This is an example of bald eagles choosing to roost in what is already public lands—Illinois' Pere Marquette State Park, located near the junction of the Illinois and Mississippi Rivers. Coves in two wooded ravines with 300 feet forested walls—Graham's Hollow and William's Hollow—afford excellent roosting protection from winter storms, while having easy access to Swan Lake and the Illinois River for feeding. In February, 1970, the number of birds using the William's Hollow roost peaked at 62.

Both the National and State Park Systems, while exerting every effort to provide protection for plant cover and the animal life occurring on each area, are nevertheless established for recreational use. The human disturbance factor is a problem each administrator lives with. The eagle roost at Pere Marquette State Park might have been lost to a ski lift had not the roost's location been brought to the attention of the administration. Now Graham's and William's Hollows receive from the Director of Illinois Department of Conservation the protection due a sensitive natural area.

Cedar Glen Eagle Roost

In 1964, Western Illinois University acquired several hundred acres of forested floodplain on the Mississippi River across from Keokuk, Iowa, to serve as a field station for teaching biological sciences. They identified an adjacent area of eroded Keokuk limestone forming a bowl with walls 75 to 100 feet high that was a night roosting area for 60 to 100 bald eagles during severe winter weather.

The Illinois Chapter of the Nature Conservancy began acquiring this area in 1970, and by 1974 the Cedar Glen Eagle Roost encompassed 423 acres of deep rocky ravines and forested flood plain, including Mink

Island (now called Eagle Island). The Illinois Chapter of The Nature Conservancy is continuing its program to enlarge this sanctuary by including important feeding areas below Lock and Dam No. 19.

WISCONSIN:

Ferry Bluff Eagle Roost

The same group that located the major night roost above Cassville, Wisconsin, and subsequently undertook the purchase and management of Eagle Valley were also responsible for spotting another night roost on private lands on the Wisconsin River near Sauk City, Wisconsin. They set to work locally to raise funds to purchase the site, but progress was distressingly slow. At this juncture the National Wildlife Federation stepped in to assist. In January, 1976, the Anheuser-Busch, Inc., presented a check for $47,000 to the National Wildlife Federation for the purchase of 150 acres at Ferry Bluff. The Federation retains ownership but has assigned management of the roost site to the people most interested—Eagle Valley Environmentalists, Inc.

In January, 1976, there were 26 bald eagles using this night roost, feeding during the day about 5 miles upstream at the dam near Prairie du Sac.

Eagle Valley

In studying the overwintering concentrations of bald eagles along the Mississippi River at Cassville, Wisconsin, Terrence Ingram noted that the birds were flying north each evening about 7 miles to roost in a 3-mile valley that parallels the Mississippi River. Here steep 350 feet bluffs create a virtual canyon with heavily wooded sides and bottom—perfect for overnight protection against winter storms.

In 1971, the Southwestern Wisconsin Audubon Club began a fund-raising campaign to purchase the valley as a conservation reserve. This organization, now reorganized as Eagle Valley Environmentalists, Inc., have under purchase or land contract 1,385 acres including both Eagle and Good'nuf Valleys. The present plan is to hold the lower 700 acres, which includes the eagle roost, as a natural area, and to develop the remainder into a nature education center.

Clarence N. Ingram, Executive Director, Eagle Valley Environmentalists, Inc.

SOUTH DAKOTA:

Karl E. Mundt National Wildlife Refuge

This 1,123 acre refuge, just downstream from the Fort Randall dam on the Missouri River, was specifically established to provide wintering sanctuary for the bald eagles. The purchase of this river bottom tract was initiated by the National Wildlife Federation who subsequently conveyed it to the U.S. Fish and Wildlife Service as a unit in the national refuge system. Some $200,000 of the purchase price came from a product promotion program of the 7-Eleven Stores. The open water below the dam even in a severe winter attracts waterfowl and is a source of fish, and thus has developed into a favorite wintering area for migrant bald eagles. In December, 1975, this refuge hosted 136 bald eagles. Karen Steenhoff has completed a two-year intensive study of bald eagles wintering on this area.

WASHINGTON:

Skagit River Bald Eagle Natural Wildlife Area

On February 6, 1976, ceremonies highlighted by the presence of Washington's Governor Evans, ushered in a new bald eagle sanctuary along the Skagit River between Rockport and Marblemont. Purchases by The Nature Conservancy, aided by land gifts from the Simpson Timber Company, the Scott Paper Company, and rancher, Fred Martin, added 532 acres to the 600 acres already owned by Washington State's Department of Game. All lands in this sanctuary will subsequently be administered by the State's Department of Game.

The Skagit River supports a spawning run of some five species of salmon which attracts a very large concentration of bald eagles each fall—the numbers depending on the size of the run on a particular year. In January, 1976, the eagles on the Skagit peaked at 148. There is an excellent two-year study of these eagles by Christopher Servheen.

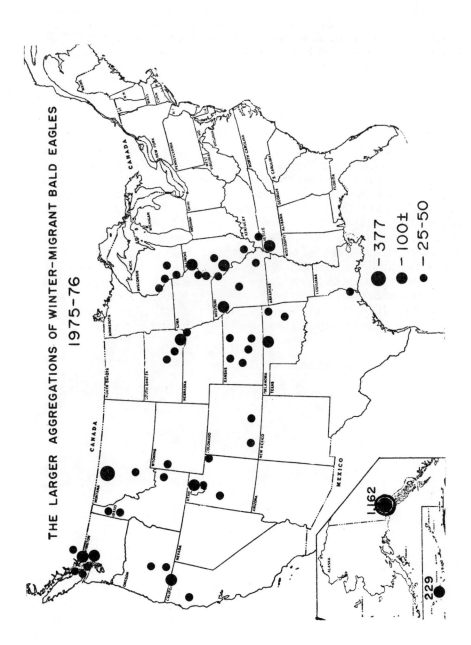

THE LARGER AGGREGATIONS OF WINTER-MIGRANT BALD EAGLES
1975-76

14
Recreation: Eagle Watching

To achieve the greatest appreciation of the bald eagle, the interested public must have the opportunity to observe this bird in the wild. We cannot provide this opportunity with our resident nesting population as they are very sensitive to intrusion during the reproductive season.

The migrant bald eagle, on the other hand, finds much of his winter larder within sight and sound of man. Like many other avian species under a drive for limited food, the bald eagle progressively adjusts to any freedom from direct harassment. Thus with proper programming the wintering bald eagle can be relatively tolerant of an audience at a respectful distance.

The winter migrant is more numerous than the summer nester, can be found in many more states and localities, and to the delight of the observer large groups rather than single individuals put on a performance.

While in general the winter "eagle watching" season extends from mid-October to mid-March, birds at any one site may be present but a fraction of that period. For example, birds have largely exhausted the supplies of spawned-out salmon in McDonald Creek and departed by mid-December, having peaked in numbers in mid-November. Even at sites having season-long food supplies, eagle numbers from week to week may change radically. So having elected to visit a given bald eagle wintering ground, the visitor is well advised to inquire well in advance as to the optimum dates.

137

Night roosts should largely be "off limits" to other than research investigators. But before first light the eagles are on their way to the feeding grounds where until about 10:00 a.m. the capture of prey, and the challenge and competition between individual eagles, will present an endless pageant. Thereafter, if food has not been too difficult to obtain, the eagles will perch quietly (like so many candles) in stream and lakeside trees, with little or no activity for hours. This pattern is broken on days when thermal updrafts of warm air develop. Instead of roosting at mid-day the entire group will take to the air, soaring to great heights in a spectacular vortex. In late afternoon, as though on signal, this "play time" ceases and the birds return for another feeding session before leaving for the night roost area.

Where a closer approach is necessary for photography, blinds can be erected with a screened approach; or better yet, the blind can be entered before first light in the morning. Normal sounds and movement within the blind appear to have no noticeable effect on eagle behavior.

The chance to watch bald eagles in the wild is proving to be such a public attraction that fully supervised programs are necessary to prevent a few unthinking individuals from intruding past the limits the eagles will tolerate.

It is hard to envision that "eagle watchers" totaling 5,608 trekked (on the weekends of October and November) to western Montana, but that's the way it was in 1975. But 377 bald eagles in a 7-mile stretch of stream is a powerful drawing card.

On an optimum day a serious birder has the opportunity to see 100 bald eagles in a single day in Alaska (of course) but also in Illinois, Missouri, Tennessee, Oklahoma, South Dakota, Montana, Idaho, Washington, and California. To spot 15-25 wintering bald eagles in a localized area would be possible in any state west of the Mississippi River, with the exception of Arizona and Nevada. East of the Mississippi River add Wisconsin, Ilinois, Kentucky, Tennessee, and one very isolated area in southern New York State.

TENNESSEE:

The state park at Reelfoot Lake began offering daily guided auto tours to see bald eagles in the winter of 1974-75. A total of 400 people participated as well as 135 who registered for Eagle Weekend 1975. Public response to Eagle Weekend 1976 was even greater. In addition to the weekend, a total of 613 people participated in daily auto tours in January and February, 1976.

Reelfoot Lake offers a unique opportunity for the public to view our national bird. The birds are abundant and obligingly perch in trees along the highway on the south end of the lake. Although the birds are easy to see without a guide, we are encouraging people to take one of our organized tours so that we can inform them about the conservation problems of the bald eagles. We also feel that supervised tours can help keep harassment of the birds to a minimum.

Next winter we plan again to offer daily auto tours. Instead of one big weekend we are considering offering a series of weekends with guest speakers. We want to accommodate as many people as possible without sacrificing quality.

> *Marilyn J. Williamson, Regional Naturalist, Division of State Parks, Tennessee Department of Conservation*

Yes, our eagles are great people attractors—probably too much so for the bird's own good. For example, we had about 900 people here on a recent weekend, specifically for viewing eagles. However, we get many people, from all points of the compass, here for eagle watching throughout the winter.

> *Wendell E. Crews, Manager, Reelfoot NWR*

Eagle watching at Reelfoot Lake in Tennessee attracts so much attention that the magazine *Southern Living,* carried a full-page sotry on the program in its January, 1976, issue. The article began:

"Just as California's Capistrano Mission has its swallows, so Reel-Reelfoot Lake in northwestern Tennessee has its bald eagles.

Arriving each November, these noble birds spend the entire winter at this shallow cypress-draped lake, feeding on fish netted (and discarded) by Reelfoot's commercial fishermen. The birds have been coming to the lake since it was formed by an earthquake around 1812..."

"Bring your camera" the information circular on Eagle Weekend 1976 urged. The park has constructed 5 blinds for photographers. These blinds will be reserved on Eagle Weekend 1976 for those who sign up at registration. At any other time they are on a first come, first served basis.

> *Reelfoot Lake Sector*

Our main attraction for visitors is the large concentration of waterfowl during November through February. However, the visitor is always delighted when an eagle is observed during his day in the field.

> *Samuel W. Barton, Manager, Cross Creeks NWR*

KENTUCKY:

The last weekend of February 250 people of all ages converged on Lake Barkley State Resort Park, near Cadiz, for the annual "Eagles Weekend." This event was sponsored jointly by the Kentucky Department of Parks and Tennessee Valley Authority's Land Between the Lakes. The program included speakers from as far away as Minnesota and featured a lake-side tour in a fleet of school buses to have a first-hand look, via binoculars and spotting scope, at the migrant bald eagles that winter here. This is the third year for this event.

From: Kentucky Happy Hunting Ground (Magazine), May 1976

OKLAHOMA:

Bald eagle use of the Sequoyah Refuge and other federal waters in this area have caused considerable interest from the local public.

Robert H. Stratton, Jr., Manager, Sequoyah NWR

Observations of Roost A (Salt Ford River, Oklahoma), were made from a blind 100 meters distant. I usually entered the blind early in the afternoon before eagles started arriving. If eagles were in the roost when I arrived, they usually left the roost and returned after I was inside the blind. Noises and movements in the blind did not appear to disturb the eagles. If I left the blind during daylight when eagles were in the roost, they would fly off. However, when I left the blind at dark, the eagles were not disturbed.

I occasionally drove a vehicle to a dirt road approximately 30 meters west of Roost A to collect pellets in the late morning when a few eagles were present. On several occasions the eagles remained until I left the vehicle.

James W. Lish, MS Thesis, Oklahoma State University, (1975)

ARKANSAS:

Our eagles are a major attraction for visitors to Holla Bend during the period that they are in the area. For some people seeing one of Holla Bends's eagles represent a first in their lifetime, and a thrill they don't mind telling us about.

Paul D. Daly, Manager, Holla Bend NWR

COLORADO:

This group of birds does attract bird watchers to the refuge.

Charles R. Bryant, Manager, Monte Vista NWR

We regularly give programs on the golden eagle to visitors at our summer campfire programs and to school groups during the winter months. Eagle observation auto tours for the public are given during March on the north shore of Blue Mesa Lake.

> *James W. Packard, Superintendent, Curecanti National Recreation Area, National Park Service*

NEW MEXICO:

The eagles are quite an attraction for our bird watchers. The eagles are frequently seen from the roads. They are easily observed and often can be photographed by those people equipped with a 400 millimeter telephoto lens.

> *Fred L. Bolwahnn, Manager, Las Vegas NWR*

These bald eagles, plus a near equal number of golden eagles, provide several hours of viewing opportunity to the public throughout the winter months. A few golden eagles may be observed year round.

> *Milton B. Suthers, Assistant Refuge Manager, Maxwell NWR*

ARIZONA:

These eagles did attract refuge visitors, particularly when we put out the word that immatures could readily be observed here at our headquarters.

> *Gerald E. Duncan, Manager, Imperial NWR*

MONTANA:

Blinds (three) were constructed of heavy white canvas over a frame of metal pipes. They blended in well with the snow but were rather obtrusive at times when snow cover was scant. This did not have any major noticeable effects on the eagles. These blinds were only about 2 feet back from the edge of the east bank of the creek where the eagles were feeding.

> *David S. Shea, MS Thesis (1973), Glacier National Park*

Each fall bald eagles assemble by the hundreds along McDonald Creek to feed on spawned-out kokanee salmon. But even more surprising is the number of people who come to watch this annual event. We counted only on weekends in October and November and noted a total of 5,608 visitors at the Apgar Bridge. The main viewpoints were Apgar and Quarter Circle Bridges over McDonald Creek.

Naturalists were on hand on weekends at the Apgar Bridge to provide information services and lead periodic guided tours (for groups of 15 or less) to the wildlife viewing blind. We have continued to operate a wildlife viewing blind downstream from the Apgar Bridge. This is available to photographers, school groups, and other organized groups for viewing and photography by reservation. Space is very limited and reservations fill up early. Reservations for use of the blind are not accepted before September 1 each year.

Charles B. Sigler, Chief Park Ranger, Glacier National Park

WASHINGTON:

The eagles of San Juan Island and vicinity are of intense local interest and have attracted many park visitors.

William Stevens, National Park Service, San Juan Island

On February 6, 1976, over 200 people, including Washington's State Governor Dan Evans, attended the dedication of a new bald eagle sanctuary on the Skagit River 5 miles east of Rockport. This year 148 bald eagles had assembled by January to feed on the spawned-out salmon. While protecting a wintering river corridor whose history reaches far back into the past, the plans do not overlook the public's need to be able to view this exciting aggregation of birds. Camouflaged trails and a viewing tower will minimize disturbance by humans.

State of Washington, Department of Game, 1976

WISCONSIN/ILLINOIS:

Eagle Valley Environmentalists, Inc., have a small booklet available for purchase entitled, *Winter Birding Along the Mississippi River* by Elton Fawks and Terrence N. Ingram.

This booklet provides explicit directions for reaching a score of observation points along the river where aggregations of bald eagles can be watched fishing, competing with one another, or perched like candles in a tree during the loafing period of the day. This section of the Mississippi River hosts at least 700 bald eagles in January.

These winter migrants have become quite accustomed to automobile traffic and will approach within 150 to 200 feet, *but only if you stay in the car.*

Elton Fawks, Eagle Research Coordinator, National Wildlife Federation (Text Condensed By Editor)

In addition to the above guide book, Eagle Valley Environmentalists, Inc., annually host Bald Eagle Days. This program features leading research and management personnel from around the nation for the purpose of updating our knowledge of this bird. Two days of lectures, reports, and films in January, 1976, were followed by field trips to the Wisconsin River near Sauk City and Prairie du Sac, Wisconsin, to see bald eagles in the wild.

Terrence N. Ingram, Executive Director, Eagle Valley Environmentalists, Inc.

PART II:

Eastern States

15
Wintering Bald Eagles
Where to Look is Important

Along the Atlantic Coast north of Florida, there are two resident (and wintering) groups of bald eagles: 1) In the Chesapeake Bay area, 2) Along the coast of Maine, and in the Maritime Provinces of Canada. The two United States populations have been intensively inventoried and total only about 250 birds. All evidence presently available to me would indicate that there is no nesting population in eastern Ontario, Quebec, and the Maritime Provinces comparable to the estimated 10,000-plus bald eagles nesting in the prairie and western provinces of Canada, and the 50,000-plus bald eagles in Alaska and the coast of British Columbia. Without such northern nesting 'back up', there is no reason to look for any large numbers of migrant bald eagles headed for wintering grounds in the eastern United States.

The population of northern bald eagles in Maine is estimated to number 40 to 50 birds. For this small number of eagles, the food supply along the coast during winter months does not sag sufficiently to force them South—with the possible exception of a group of 10 to 12 bald eagles that move inland to Massachusetts' Quabbin Reservoir to feed on big game carrion.

Where the twenty-odd bald eagles wintering on hydroelectric impoundments in Sullivan County, New York, originate from is still an open question.

The bald eagles wintering in the Chesapeake Bay area are nesting and defending territories from December through March. Even earlier (November) the bald eagles in Florida, in the coastal counties of Louisiana and Texas, and in southcentral Arizona are preparing to nest. During this period it is important that the public, including well-meaning bird watchers and photographers, minimize their intrusion into these nesting areas. By April, their 'housekeeping' finished for that year, these birds may wander as far North as the Maritime Provinces. In the fall they begin their return well before the northern nesting bald eagles have to seek relief from winter food shortages. But again, we are talking about very limited numbers of birds widely dispersed in the summer.

Each fall thousands of very dedicated people staff observation stations and scan the skies during daylight hours for raptors winging South. Their records show that a trickle of bald eagles join this throng, but only a trickle. This information is supported in turn by the fact that resident managers in the federal system of wildlife refuges in the Atlantic and eastern Gulf States observe no measurable increase in bald eagle numbers during winter months. National Forests in northcentral and northeastern states record almost no eagles wintering there.

The mid-winter waterfowl/bald eagle inventory turns up no numbers that cannot largely be accounted for by resident birds. This is not to say that there are no migrant bald eagles—just too few to provide most people a chance to get acquainted.

The Christmas Bird Counts of 482 participating local Audubon Societies in the 25 eastern states were not intended as a 'population census'. The count circles are not positioned with the habitat of any one bird species in mind. For example, the 42 count circles in New York State recorded only three bald eagles, missing the aggregation of twenty birds in Sullivan County. Similarly, the 21 count circles in Massachusetts discovered only one bald eagle when 10 to 12 were wintering on Quabbin Reservoir. Nevertheless, this annual Audubon Christmas Bird Count lends emphasis to the fact that outside of the four nesting locations along the Atlantic Coast wintering bald eagles are few.

While people in the eastern states have little opportunity to engage in 'eagle watching', the opposite is true from the Mississippi valley to the Pacific northwest. For a four to five month period, the western two-thirds of this nation plays host to amazing numbers of bald eagles that obligingly form spectacular groups which are relatively tolerant of a respectful audience.

16
Fall 1974, Hawk Migration Records

New England: 58 Observation Posts
 September 14, 1974: 8,435 raptors sighted, includes 4 bald eagles
 September 15, 1974: 25,494 raptors sighted, includes 3 bald eagles

Montclair, New Jersey:
 13 migrating bald eagles, season-long

Cape May, New Jersey: August 25-November 30
 22,762 raptors recorded, including 4 juvenile bald eagles (between August 25-September 12)

Hawk Mt., Pennsylvania: August-December
 32,155 raptors recorded, including only 18 bald eagles

Hawk Cliffs (North Shore, Lake Erie): August-December
 40,983 raptors recorded, including only 5 bald eagles

Hawk Ridge (Duluth, Minnesota): August 26-November 29
 49,918 raptors recorded, including 95 bald eagles

Journal of Hawk Migration Association of North America Vol. 1, No. 1, May 1975

17

Northeastern National Wildlife Refuges

MICHIGAN:

Records from recent years indicate that neither Seney NWR nor Huron Islands NWR host wintering bald eagles. We occasionally have individuals appear for a day or two on the area during January. Our nesting eagles generally reappear in mid-February. There are really no records of observations for the area of the Huron Islands so that is an unknown.

John R. Frye, Manager, Seney NWR

OHIO:

The northern bald eagle is the only eagle which is regularly seen at Ottawa NWR. Records from 1969 to the present indicate a maximum of six at any one time. One pair nests on the refuge and raised two young last year out of a total of three produced in Ohio. The third eagle was produced in this area also. The fact that six eagles have been seen here should probably be attributed to local movement rather than migration. The eagles in this area appear to be year-round residents.

With regard to migration the following is a quote from *Birds of the Toledo Area* by Lou Campbell: "Formerly, a pronounced movement took place in spring and fall from March 17 to April 16, and August 31 to October 31, but this is barely noticeable now."

James M. Carroll, Jr., Manager, Ottawa NWR

NEW YORK:

The area is in Sullivan County, approximately 6 miles southwest of Monticello, New York, and about 80 miles from New York City.

The area has been used by wintering eagles for many years; but prior to 1950, there were apparently few observers reporting eagle sightings. Since the founding of the Sullivan County Audubon Society in 1950 there have been more observers afield each year and eagles have been seen every year. The largest numbers seen to date were in January of 1973 when one group of observers counted 18 eagles in the Rio-Mongaup (area of the Mongaup River between the Rio and Mongaup Reservoirs) area, and another group counted 21 in the same area plus two at the Roundout Reservoir. The numbers fluctuate from year to year. The peak period is apparently in January.

The lakes or reservoirs along the river contain alewives, which appear to be the primary food source and the main reason for eagle concentrations in this area. The operation of the power plants at the dams insure some open water and excellent feeding conditions for the birds.

Lawrence P. Brown, Asso. Wildl. Biol., Div. Fish and Wildlife, N.Y. State Dept. of Environmental Conservation

On January 14, 1973, Audubon observers recorded 21-24 bald eagles at the Rio-Mongaup Reservoir complex. The next winter, December 17, 1973, still another Audubon team recorded 21 bald eagles in the same area. Orange and Rockland Utility employees, who have the opportunity to make more frequent observations, report highs of 28 bald eagles.

While die-off of Alewives, the winter of 1972-73 and again in 1973-74, were utilized heavily by the bald eagles, the introduction of these small fish occurred after the eagles selected the area for wintering. Ducks and deer carrion are mentioned as alternate foods.

Monticello Audubon Society: Field Observations & Comments

Iroquois NWR usually does not have favorable habitat for wintering bald eagles. Our pools are frozen during mid-winter, and we usually have few if any wintering waterfowl. Since 1972, we have only one record of a bald eagle during the period mid-October to mid-March. This was a single individual (an immature) reported on January 8, 1972, by a New York State Wildlife Technician.

John S. Morse, Wildlife Biologist, Iroquois NWR

The following are sightings of Bald Eagles on Montezuma National Wildlife Refuge since 1971 during the period of October 15 through March 15. The eagles are usually found on the northern section of the refuge, which is visited intermittently during the winter months:

November 14, 1971	1 (?)
January 1, 1973	1 immature
November 27, 1974	1 immature
January 15, 1975	1 immature
February 28, 1975	1 adult

Usually, they are observed only for a day or two during that period of time.

Sam J. Waldstein, Manager, Montezuma NWR

We have no local aggregations of wintering bald eagles on State managed conservation areas. We do have a small bald eagle wintering population of approximately 20 birds in southern New York located on privately owned land in Sullivan County.

Herbert E. Doig, Director, Division of Fish & Game, Department of Environmental Conservation

MAINE:

As near as I can determine from our own observations, Moosehorn and vicinity does not experience a "surge" of wintering birds during the mid-October to mid-March period. We generally have up to 5-6 birds in the area during that time span; however, most of them are observed on the refuge when open water is present, i.e., feeding opportunities. We suspect one active nest on the refuge; several others lie north of us along the St. Croix River valley.

Edwin H. Chandler, Manager, Moosehorn NWR

MASSACHUSETTS:

This area rarely sees migrant or wintering bald eagles in any significant numbers. It is a red-letter day when one is recorded at any time. Quite often a year will go by when none are recorded at all. Those that are seen are usually noted enroute south in the fall (October, November) migration period, much less often in the winter. Past records at this station pretty well historically support the sporadic pattern of observations of eagles at least since the establishment of the refuge.

George W. Gavutis, Jr., Manager, Parker River NWR, Newburyport, Massachusetts

I have been observing the wintering population of eagles at Quabbin for the past 23 years. The pattern has pretty much been the same with one change in later years.

Normally we see our first wintering bird in late November and from then on the numbers build to a peak in March. With ice out in April, the birds disappear. Many years ago (early 50's) we had a count as high as 25 birds which steadily declined to as low as three birds six or seven years ago. This has built up again to what I call the average of 10 or 11 birds.

Last year I had a definite count of nine bald eagles and two goldens. The age ratio on the balds was five immatures to four adults. This year my definite count was 12 balds and two goldens. The bald ratio was 10 adult and only two immature. It always makes me feel good to have many immatures, however, I do not believe that we should draw any conclusions on nesting success from these observations. There are just too many variables. The change I observed is that two adult birds have stayed through winter and summer for the past three years. No nest has been found, but everybody is hoping. Last summer a juvenile was also present, but judging from plumage it was not a bird of the year.

Jack Swedberg, Massachusetts Division of Fisheries & Game

Neither Great Meadows, Monomoy or Oxbow, the three refuges under our administration have any wintering populations of bald eagles. Occasionally an eagle will stop at Monomoy or Great Meadows during the spring migrations but never for longer than two or three days. Our record for eagles is scant as they are so infrequent.

Linda K. Gintoli, Manager, Great Meadows NWR

NEW JERSEY:

1975: One during December and January. 1974: None sighted. 1973: Six during December and January. 1972: Four during November, December, and January. 1971: Two during November through January.

Gaylord L. Inman, Manager, Brigantine NWR

MARYLAND:

The bald eagle population on Blackwater National Wildlife Refuge and adjoining lands remains fairly constant year-round at from 15-25 birds.

I cannot say that we do or do not host some winter migrants, however, our census reports show all eagles here as southern bald.

William J. Julian, Manager, Blackwater NWR

18
Southeastern National Wildlife Refuges

SOUTH CAROLINA:

Bald eagles have been recorded as wintering in this area since Savannah Refuge was established in 1927. In the early years of the refuge (30's and 40's) as many as eight eagles were seen during the peak of the waterfowl season, usually January. However, in more recent years the wintering population has been 1-3 of these birds, generally 2 adults and 1 immature. In most years, eagles were first observed in the month of November and last seen in late March. However, year-round observations in several past years of 2 adult eagles (as recent as 1974) indicates a very good chance of a nesting pair in the vicinity. No nest has been located.

John P. Davis, Manager, Savannah-Tybee Island NWR

I have checked our files for the period 1972-1976. Bald Eagle populations for this five-year period have remained relatively constant at Santee. There has been no seasonal surge and little fluctuation from quarter to quarter. I feel that these figures probably represent a local population.

Charles W. Strickland, Manager, Santee NWR

GEORGIA:

The bald eagle is listed as a rare visitor to Okefenokee during the Fall, Winter, and Spring. An eagle sighting on Okefenokee is an event to be remembered because such a sighting is so very unusual. One or two eagles a year and then for only one or two days pretty well summarizes Okefenokee's eagle activity. There are no eagle nests on the refuge.

John R. Eadie, Manger, Okefenokee NWR

ALABAMA:

Eagle use on Eufaula Refuge is sporadic and does not seem to follow a specific pattern.

Eagles will appear on the refuge, stay a few days, and then move on. Sightings occur throughout the year with the exception of the summer months. Sightings occurred this past year in September, October, November, December, January, and February.

Jimmie L. Tisdale, Manager, Eufaula NWR

Wheeler has never had the eagle numbers reported at Tennessee and Reelfoot Refuges. We once had at least one pair of bald eagles nesting regularly on the refuge, though this has not occurred since 1947. They were always uncommon through the really warm weather months, May through September, and now seem totally absent during that period. They were once reasonably common throughout the cooler months with 10 to 15 regularly using the refuge, but the numbers have been much diminished during the past 15 to 20 years. Now, we have only a few sightings during fall, winter, and early spring. During this past period,

1975-76, for example, we had only a single bird, an immature, sighted rather frequently from October 6 through January 18. There was also a lone mature bird sighted on February 24.

There were no sightings at all in the fall of 1974. The first sighting in the fall of 1973 came on October 14. In the fall of 1972 on November 15. In the fall of 1972 on September 21, and we could continue to go backward in our records if you wish. Going back over our records for the past ten years, the peak month seems to be December, though most of the December sightings were in late December. As we have said before, we once had 10 to 15 on the refuge in winter, but our highest peak in the past ten years has been 4.

Concerning winter numbers declining, they are seldom seen here after February now. Going backward through our records, the last sighting this year was February 24, February 15, 1975, January 10, 1974, no date after December 18 in 1973, and no date after December 20, 1972. We could continue back in our files as far as you like. As for observations in previous years, we have rather detailed records of eagle sightings dating back to the establishment of the refuge in 1938.

Thomas Z. Atkeson, Manager, Wheeler NWR

At present time we have very few bald eagle sight records in this state. We do have a record of five bald eagles (four adults and one juvenile) that were sighted on Guntersville Reservoir northeast of Scottsboro, Alabama, Jackson County on March 19, 1976. These were reported by two conservation officers and they reported that these birds had been present for over two weeks. This constitutes the only sight record of bald eagles that I am aware of this year.

James E. Keeler, Chief Game Research, Alabama Department of Conservation and Natural Resources

MISSISSIPPI:

Station records covering the period from 1956 through 1975 reveal that only on varied occasions have bald eagles spent time of any significance at Yazoo. They have appeared as singles and/or pairs on a few occasions, usually from mid-January through mid-March.

James M. Dale, Manager, Yazoo NWR

For the last four years, there has been a maximum of two bald eagles on Noxubee NWR. This year we only had one immature. They may stay only a few days or for two months.

Travis H. McDaniel, Manager, Noxubee NWR

19

Wintering Bald Eagles on
Eastern National Forests

REGION 9 NATIONAL FORESTS:

With the exception of the Shawnee National Forest and its vicinity in Illinois, the National Forests are not particularly important winterings areas for the bald eagle in the North Midwest and Northeastern parts of the United States.

Norman Weeden, Dir., Rec., Range, Wildl. & Landscape Mgmt. Region 9 NF

MONONGAHELA NATIONAL FOREST

Our report for the Monongahela is totally negative. We know of no wintering bald eagles.

Some sightings of golden eagles have been made. Copies of two instances are documented in the attached copy made from the March-April-May 1976 issue of the "Mail Bag" published by the Brooks Bird Club. Another golden eagle was collected in the western part of West Virginia, by the Department of Natural Resources. It was also taken to the Franch Creek Game Farm for medical treatments. This happened within the last two weeks.

Arnold F. Schulz, Wildlife Biologist, Monongahela NF

NICOLET NATIONAL FOREST:

No wintering aggregations of bald eagles are known to occur on the Nicolet. Random observations of single bald eagles have been made every month of the year.

My northernmost observation in midwinter is an adult bald eagle on Lac Vieux Desert (Michigan border) on 12/31/73. There was no open water. The bird was feeding on small fish left by ice fishermen.

Larry D. Martoglio, Wildl. Biol., Nicolet NF

OTTAWA NATIONAL FOREST:

We have heard of two instances where eagles are reported to overwinter in this area:

Watersmeet Area. A few years ago when local deer herds were at higher population levels and winter-kill and highway-kill were common, it was reported that eagles were observed throughout the winter feeding on road kills along US-2 in the vicinity of Marenisco and Watersmeet, Michigan. However, the last three years of observation indicate that eagles leave this area in the fall, returning about February 1 each year. During February and March, before the lakes thaw in April, reports of eagles feeding on road-kill deer or perched in trees adjacent to highways are common.

Baraga Area. We have one report of an eagle remaining this past winter in the vicinity of Baraga, Michigan, on Keweenaw Bay of Lake

Superior. This is a reliable report from John Hendrickson, Wildlife Habitat Biologist, District 1, Michigan DNR.
Alan D. Wilm, Wildl. Staff Officer, Ottawa NF

ALLEGHENY NATIONAL FOREST:

We have no wintering aggregation of bald eagles on the Allegheny National Forest at the present time. Occasional eagles have been observed in the vicinity of the Allegheny Reservoir in October and November.
John P. Butt, Forest Supervisor, Allegheny NF

CHEQUAMEGON NATIONAL FOREST:

Only occasionally are eagles observed during the winter in the area of the Chequamegon National Forest. As the lakes and rivers become ice covered, eagles move out. Most birds leave this area by Christmas and do not return until early March, depending on weather. The mild weather in February, 1976, opened some of the major rivers and a few eagle observations were reported. Periodically, we get reports of eagles being observed feeding on dead deer during midwinter. Such observations are not considered normal.
Richard C. Trochlil, Wild. Staff Officer, Chequamegon NF

CHIPPEWA NATIONAL FOREST:

A few adult eagles spend the winter on or near the Chippewa National Forest. These birds are always associated with open water behind dams, or "spring holes" in lakes. We have not observed any aggregations of adult or juvenile eagles in the winter or during migration.
Marlin Q. Hughes, Timber/Wildlife Staff Officer, Chippewa NF

GREEN MOUNTAIN NATIONAL FOREST:

No wintering eagles have been identified on the Green Mountain National Forest.
L. Kent Mays, Jr., Forest Supervisor

SUPERIOR NATIONAL FOREST:

We have not observed eagle wintering aggregations in northeastern Minnesota. In recent discussions with Jan Green, we both have observed individual bald eagles throughout the winter in this area, but 2 or 4 would be the usual winter's report. Several eagles have been observed wintering in the St. Croix River floodplain below Duluth. Eagles have also been observed along the North Shore of Lake Superior in December and early March.
M. L. McManigle, Wildl. Staff Officer, Superior NF

20

Audubon Christmas Bird Count 1974–Eastern States

75th Audubon Christmas Bald Eagle Count (December 1974)
From: American Birds 29 (2): April 1975

Michigan (32
Allegan State Game Area—4
Monroe—1

Indiana (21)
Indiana Dunes National
  Lakeshore—1
Nashville—2
Oakland City—1

Ohio (47)
Firelands—1
Gypsum—1
Ottawa Wildlife Refuge—2

Pennsylvania (43)
Linesville—1

New York (42)
Clinton—1
Monticello—3*

Vermont (10)
Burlington—2
Ferrisburg—1

Canada: Eastern

Newfoundland (4)
Gros Morne National Park—1
St. Anthony—1
Terra Nova National Park—6

Nova Scotia (16)
Halifax (East)—3
Halifax (West)—1
Margaree—3
St. Peters—1
Yarmouth—1

Maine (18)
Bangor-Bucksport—4
Bath-Phillipsburg—1
Blue Hill—2
East Machias—1
Mt. Desert Island—9
Orono-Old Town—1
Schoodic Point—1
Thomaston-Rockland—1

New Hampshire (12)
Baker Valley—1
Coastal—1

Massachusetts (21)*
Martha's Vineyard—1

Rhode Island (3)
None

Connecticut (15)
New Haven—4

Long Island, N.Y. (11)
Central Suffolk County—2

New Jersey (32)
Cumberland County—1

Delaware (5)
Bombay Hook NWR—3

Maryland (20)
Annapolis-Gibson Island—2
Crisfield—1
Denton—1
Elkton—1
Lower Kent County—4
Ocean City—3
Point Lookout—4
Rock Run—1
Salisbury—1
South Dorchester County—35

Virginia (29)
Brooke—3
Chincoteague—2
Fort Belvoir—1
Hopewell—1
Mathews—3

West Virginia (11)
None

North Carolina (20)
None

South Carolina (5)
None

Georgia (14)
None

Florida (34)
Bradenton—4
Cocoa—1
Coot Bay-Everglades National
    Park—34
Dade County—1
Ft. Lauderdale—1
Ft. Meyers—12
Ft. Pierce—2
Gainesville—8
Jacksonville—1
Key Lago-Plantation Key—3
Kissimmee Valley—10
Lakeland—2
Lake Wales—4
Lower Keys—3
Merritt Island NWR—11
Myakka River State Park—7
Naples—10
New Port Richey—1
St. Marks—4
St. Petersburg—2
Sanibel & Captiva Islands—2
Saratoga—2
South Brevard County—2
Stuart—2
Venice-Englewood—5

Alabama (9)
Wheeler—1

Mississippi (8)
Jackson—1

21

Mid-Winter Waterfowl/ Bald Eagle Inventory Eastern United States

MICHIGAN:

According to Edward Mikula, Waterfowl Specialist, no eagles were recorded during the mid-winter waterfowl census.
Victor S. Janson, South Michigan Game Bird Management, Michigan DNR

PENNSYLVANIA:

There were no bald eagles found wintering in Pennsylvania during the recent mid-winter waterfowl census nor were they found wintering in recent years. Not much wintering habitat occurs in southern Pennsylvania. A single bird resided on the Middle Creek Waterfowl Management Area for a portion of 1975.
Dale E. Sheffer, Chief, Division of Game Management, Pennsylvania Game Commission

We had two immature bald eagles on the area from December, 1974 to late April, 1975. The one appeared to be a year older than the other and could be seen most every day. The second one was seen two to three times per week and the two were seen together quite often on the same tree. The last time that I saw the older one it had almost complete adult plumage. We have not seen either one of them this past winter.
Charles L. Strouphar, Manager, Middlecrek WMA

MAINE:

Before we made some effort to determine the wintering area of our eagles, we felt they most probably migrated south along the Atlantic seaboard for at least a short period in winter. There were always a few eagles scattered in the major estuaries, but they seemed too few to represent the whole population.

In the past several years, we have intensified our summer survey and have more confidence in our population estimates. During this winter and last winter (1974-1975), we participated in a more widespread search for wintering eagles. I now believe that essentially all our breeding eagles winter along the Maine-New Brunswick coast. In 1975, with very limited resources, our winter survey, admittedly incomplete, projected 65 wintering eagles on the Maine coast in January. The gaps in the data could very well include all our birds (100+).

Observations at coastal nest sites indicated that birds might be present in the area on any given day of the year. No large concentrations were noted anywhere. Three to seven bird "concentrations" occurred at primary feeding areas. The highest reported concentration was nine birds (six adults, three immatures) on the Penobscot at a feeding station in Orrington.

Sightings were rather randomly scattered from St. Stephens, New Brunswick to Portland, Maine, and a scattering of sightings reported to as far inland as Millinocket. The most dependable winter concentrations occur on the Penobscot in the Bangor area and in the Kennebec above Bath, but a search of any of the major bays of offshore island groups will generally yield a wintering eagle sighting.

As far as I can determine, the Maine coast, Quabbin Reservoir, and the Westchester County New York site have the only regularly occurring winter eagle concentrations in the New York-New England area.

I feel that there is little evidence of a flow to Maine from northern areas. I do believe that we may receive a small number of immatures from other areas.

Francis J. Gramlich, U.S. Fish & Wildlife Service

NEW YORK:

A thirteen-year list of records in New York State of bald eagle sightings during annual mid-winter waterfowl surveys.

Year	Birds Observed	Areas
1976	1 Immature	St. Lawrence River area
1975	None	
1975	1 Adult/1 Immature	St. Lawrence River area/Lake Ontario
1973	None	
1972	None	
1971	2 Adults	St. Lawrence River area/Lake Ontario
1970	1 Adult	St. Lawrence River area
1969	None	
1968	4 Adults	St. Lawrence River area/Lake Champlain
1967	None	
1966	None	
1965	None	
1964	6 Adults	St. Lawrence River area/Lake Ontario/ Lake Champlain

Herbert E. Doig, Director, Division of Fish & Game, Department of Environmental Conservation

MID-WINTER WATERFOWL/BALD EAGLE INVENTORY

States	1975	1976
Michigan	2	—
Indiana	3	1
Ohio	8	4
Pennsylvania	1	2
New York	—	2
Vermont	—	—
New Hampshire	—	—
Maine	12	4
Massachusetts	—	—
Rhode Island	—	—
Connecticut	—	—
New Jersey	—	5
Delaware	—	3
Maryland	10	17
Virginia	—	10
West Virginia	—	—
North Carolina	2	—
South Carolina	17	16
Georgia	—	—
Florida	28	46
Alabama	1	2
Mississippi	1	1
Total	85	113

From: Files of Migratory Bird Management Office, Washington, D.C.

PART III:

Intensive Studies on Wintering Bald Eagles

WASHINGTON:

Stalmaster, Mark and Dr. James Newman. 1975-
Project in progress: A study of the specific habitat requirements
of wintering bald eagles along the Nooksack River in northwest
Washington.
Huxley College of Environmental Studies

Servheen, Christopher Walter. 1975
Ecology of the Wintering Bald Eagles on the Skagit River, Wash-
ington.
(Two-year field study completed)
MS Thesis, 82 pages, University of Washington (unpublished)

English, Walter, 1976-
Project in progress: A study of bald eagle movements through
marking birds released from a rehabilitation program at Seattle
Woodland Park Zoo.

IDAHO:

Lint, Joseph B. 1976-
The Bald Eagles of Wolf Lodge Bay.
Bureau of Land Management, Coeur d'Alene, Idaho.
*(Note: A continuing project by the author of Wintering Bald
Eagles on National Resource Lands in the Lake Coeur d'Alene
Area.)*

UTAH:

Edwards, Clyde C. 1969
Winter Behavior and Population Dynamics of American Eagles in
Western Utah. Unpublished PhD Thesis.
Brigham Young University, Provo, Utah.
(Field work covers three successive winters 1966-69)

Joseph, Ronald A. 1976-
Wintering Populations of Bald Eagles in the Great Basin.
*A graduate study underway at Brigham Young University under
the supervision of Dr. Joseph R. Murphy*

MONTANA:

Shea, David S. 1973
A Management-oriented Study of Bald Eagle Concentrations in
Glacier National Park.
(Two-year field study completed)
MS Thesis, 78 pages, University of Montana (unpublished)

WYOMING:

Swenson, Jon Eugene. 1975
Ecology of the Bald Eagle and Osprey in Yellowstone National Park.
(Two-year field study completed)
MS Thesis, 146 pages, Montana State University (unpublished)

SOUTH DAKOTA:

Steenhof, Karen. 1974-75
Ecological Study of Bald Eagles Wintering on Lake Andes and Karl E. Mundt National Wildlife Refuges, Missouri River.
(Two-year field work completed, manuscript in preparation.)
Gaylord Memorial Laboratory, Puxico, Missouri

MISSOURI:

Griffin, Curtis, 1975-77
Ecology of Bald Eagles Wintering in Missouri with Emphasis on Eagle/Waterfowl Relationships.
A field project begun in October, 1975, at Swan Lake National Wildlife Refuge with completion scheduled for spring of 1977.
Missouri Cooperative Wildlife Research Unit, University of Missouri

OKLAHOMA:

Lish, James William. 1975
Status and Ecology of Bald Eagles and Nesting of Golden Eagles in Oklahoma.
(Two-year field study completed)
MS Thesis, 98 pages, Oklahoma State University (unpublished)

CANADA: British Columbia:

Hancock, David. 1964
Bald Eagles Wintering in the Southern Gulf Islands, British Columbia.
Project completed)
The Wilson Bulletin 76: 111-120, 1964

CANADA: Nova Scotia:

Gittens, Edward Francis. 1968
A Study on the Status of the Bald Eagle in Nova Scotia.
(Project completed)
MS Thesis, Acadia University

CANADA: Maritime Provinces:

Stocek, R. F. 1974 and 1975
The Bald Eagle, Osprey, and Peregrine Falcon in the Maritime Provinces.
The two-year investigation and its preliminary reports are presently being organized into a formal manuscript.
Study undertaken under contract with the Canadian Wildlife Service.
The Maritime Forest Ranger School, University of New Brunswick, Fredericton

ILLINOIS:

Southern, William E. 1963
Winter Populations, Behavior, and Seasonal Dispersal of Bald Eagles in Northwestern Illinois.
The Wilson Bulletin 75(1): 42-55 March of 1963

Jonen, J. R. 1973
The Winter Ecology of the Bald Eagle in Westcentral Illinois.
MS Thesis, 84 pages, Western Illinois University, Macomb, Illinois

Dunstan, Thomas C. 1974
The Status and Role of Bald Eagle Winter Studies in the Midwest.
Proceedings: Bald Eagle Days Symposium 1974.
Western Illinois University, Macomb, Illinois
(Note: Dr. Dunstan is author or coauthor of numerous other studies on bald eagles in the upper Mississippi basin.)

Harper, James F. 1976
Dispersal and Migration of Fledgling Bald Eagles.
Presented at: 1976 Bald Eagle Days, Madison, Wisconsin
Western Illinois University, Macomb, Illinois

_____1974
Activities of Fledgling Bald Eagles in North-Central Minnesota.
MS Thesis, 68 pages, Western Illinois University, Macomb, Illinois